WEST HAM UNITED

C000151818

QUIZ
BOOK

Published by twocan

©2018. Published by twocan under licence from West Ham United FC.

ISBN: 978-1-912692-48-4

PICTURE CREDITS: Getty Images

COMPILED BY ROB MASON

INTRODUCTION

I first visited West Ham in 1978 and have always known the club to be supported by some of the most passionate fans in the country. This set of 100 quizzes includes some questions that everyone is likely to know, some that will stretch the grey matter a little and some that will tease even the Irons die-hards amongst you.

I've sometimes made questions multi-choice but not always. Some questions have answers that are simple facts that if you don't know without a prompt, it's time to learn. Hopefully this book will entertain you and ideally make you realise a few things that you might not know even if you are a West Ham brain-box.

What comes out of many of these quizzes is how many tremendously dedicated players and managers the club has had throughout its history. That is a testament to the club itself and what it represents in the community. Taking on this book shows you are a similarly dedicated supporter.

The quizzes cover a wide range of the club's players, managers and major events. It is not a guide to the club though so your favourite player might not have a quiz dedicated solely to him.

See how many of the 1000 questions you can get right. Can you get 500 correct? If so you'll have achieved a decent score. There are 20 teams in the Premier League and 1000 questions here. If you are to take on the challenge of doing as well as possible take it that for every 50 points you manage - it is always one point per question - you achieve one place in the league table, i.e. 50 points out of 1000 would see you in 20th place, 100 would take you to 19th, 150 to 18th and so on.

I'd like to acknowledge many sources, including, Rothmans / Sky Sports Yearbooks, John Northcutt and Roy Shoesmith's West Ham United, A Complete Record, Breedon's brilliant 'Football Managers' book, my own Farewell Boleyn book and the England Online website which is evidently a labour of love.

Rob Mason

MARKO ARNAUTOVIC

1.   Who did West Ham sign Marko from?

2.   Which country was Arnautovic born in?

3.   Which famous Italian team was he once on loan to?

4.   Which German club did he play for?

5.   Against which club did Arnautovic make his West Ham debut?

6.   He scored his first goal for the Hammers to win a London derby, against which club?

7.   In his first season at West Ham Marko scored eleven Premier League goals. Who was the last Hammers player to reach that total?

8.   In 2006 Marko scored twice in an international match against which home country?

9.   What did Marko do at West Ham in April 2015?

10. Which individual award did Marko win in his first season at the club?

11. How many times was Trevor Hammer of the Year?

12. Which manager had taken seriously ill when Brooking stepped in as caretaker-manager in 2003?

13. In which position did Trevor play when he made his West Ham debut in a 3-3 draw with Burnley in 1967?

14. What connects Bobby Moore, Frank Lampard Senior and Billy Bonds with regard to Brooking?

15. Did Trevor score over or under 100 goals for West Ham?

16. The most goals Brooking scored in one season for West Ham was eleven - in which season?

17. In which year did he head the match-winning goal in the FA Cup final?

18. Did he win over or under 50 caps for England?

19. In which year did Trevor play his final game for the Irons?

20. Which of these nicknames was never assigned to Sir Trevor at West Ham: 'Cyril', 'Boog,' 'Brooks' or 'Hadleigh'?

QUIZ 3
FRANK LAMPARD SENIOR

21. Which position did Frank Lampard Senior star in?

22. How many times did Frank win the FA Cup with West Ham?

23. Which club did he finish his career with after long service with West Ham?

24. Which of his old Hammers teammates did he play for at his second club?

25. Who was manager when Frank returned to West Ham as assistant manager?

26. Which future Liverpool and Celtic manager did Lampard senior later work with at Watford and Reading?

27. Which ex-England, Liverpool, Spurs and Southampton player is Frank Senior's nephew?

28. How many times did Frank Senior play for England?

29. Which former West Ham manager gave Frank his final England cap?

30. In their overall careers who made most league appearances, Frank Senior or Frank Junior?

QUIZ 4
FRANK LAMPARD JUNIOR

31. Which club did Frank Lampard Junior join on loan from West Ham before his Hammers debut?

32. Which club did Frank Junior make his West Ham debut against?

33. Lampard Junior scored his first hat-trick for West Ham against Walsall, in which competition?

34. Frank was ever-present as West Ham reached a highest-ever league position of fifth, in which season?

35. Who were the French side Frank scored against in the final of the Intertoto Cup in August 1999?

36. Who were the opponents when Frank and Paolo Di Canio had a wrestling match over who was to take a penalty in what proved to be a 5-4 win?

37. Which former West Ham player and manager is Frank's uncle?

38. Did Frank play over or under 100 games for England?

39. With which American club did Frank finish his playing days?

40. Which club did he take up a first managerial position with in 2018?

QUIZ 5
ANDRIY YARMOLENKO

41. Who was Andriy signed from for a reported fee of £17.5m in 2018?

42. With which club did he play almost 300 games?

43. Yarmolenko is an international for which country?

44. Which UK team did he play against at Euro 2012?

45. Andriy has an international hat-trick to his name, true or false?

46. Who did he make his West Ham debut against?

47. How many times has he been Footballer of the Year in his home country?

48. In 2016 he scored the winner in an international match against which British country, who had Wayne Hennessey in goal?

49. Who did he score against at Wembley in 2017?

50. His final club goal before signing for West Ham was against which former European champions?

51. Bobby Moore had two middle names. One is also the name of a football team, which one?

52. Was England's World Cup winning skipper awarded the MBE, OBE or CBE?

53. Did he win 108, 118 or 128 caps for England?

54. Which future Manchester City and Crystal Palace manager did he come on as substitute for when he made his debut for West Ham?

55. How old was Bobby when he became England's youngest captain?

56. What individual honour did Moore win in 1964 as he captained West Ham to the FA Cup?

57. In the year Moore captained England in the World Cup final he also scored in cup final for West Ham, in which competition?

58. What linked Poland and Norway in Moore's international career?

59. Moore captained England 90 times. Which captain's record did he equal?

60. Who did he play for against West Ham in an FA Cup final?

QUIZ 7
ISSA DIOP

61. Who was Issa Diop signed from?

62. Although the fee when Diop was signed was undisclosed, it was described as a club record. At the time would this have made the fee in excess of £10m, £20m or £30m?

63. Who did Diop make his West Ham debut against?

64. Which club did Issa score his first goal against?

65. In which competition was that goal scored?

66. At the time of his arrival at West Ham which country had he played for at all levels from Under 16 to Under 21?

67. Due to his parents, Diop is eligible to play for Morocco and which other African country?

68. Diop's final goal for the club West Ham signed him from was against the club his grandfather used to play for. Which club is that?

69. Is he taller or smaller than Winston Reid and Andy Carroll?

70. Which newly promoted club did Diop make his home debut against?

QUIZ 8
RON GREENWOOD

71. In what year did Ron Greenwood become manager of West Ham United?

72. Which club had Greenwood played for when they won the league title?

73. Which of the following clubs did Ron not play for: Bradford, Brentford, Doncaster or Fulham?

74. Which London club was Greenwood coaching while also managing England at Under 23 level?

75. How many cup finals did Greenwood lead West Ham to in his first six years at the club?

76. Who did he take over from as England manager?

77. Who became West Ham team manager when Ron became general manager of West Ham?

78. Was Ron born in Burnley, Bradford or Bolton?

79. As a youngster, at which football stadium did Ron work as an apprentice sign-writer?

80. Greenwood was captain on his one international appearance, at which level?

QUIZ 9
LUKASZ FABIANSKI

81. Which other English club has Fabianski played for?

82. Which was the last club in his home country
     he played for?

83. Which international team does Fabianski play for?

84. Which manager brought Fabianski into British football?

85. In which year did Fabianski concede two goals
     in the first eight minutes of the FA Cup final against
     Hull City but gain a winner's medal?

86. Fabianski's birthday is 18 April. In which year was he born?

87. Before moving into British football which future
     Southampton and Bournemouth goalkeeper did
     he compete with at club level?

88. How many cup games did Fabianski play in the four
     years before joining West ham: zero, one or ten?

89. With which club was Fabianski Player of the Year
     in 2017/18?

90. Which club did Fabianski make his West Ham
     Premier League debut against?

QUIZ 10
SIR GEOFF HURST

91. Who did Geoff score a hat-trick against for England in the 1966 World Cup final?

92. Who did he score a double hat-trick against for West Ham in 1968?

93. Apart from England which other European country did he play in?

94. Which southern hemisphere country did he play in?

95. Which club did he finish his career with?

96. How many caps did he win for England: 49, 59 or 89?

97. With which County did he play first class cricket for?

98. In which overseas country did he manage?

99. Which London club did he manage?

100. Which club did West Ham sell him to in 1972?

QUIZ 11
JOHN SISSONS

101. In which season did Sissons become Wembley's youngest FA Cup final scorer?

102. Which other final did he score in in the same year at international level?

103. How many goals did Sissons score in his 265 games for West Ham: 55, 83 or 103?

104. Which club bought John in 1970?

105. Which club was his last in England?

106. Which other English club did he play for?

107. Which American club did he go on loan to in 1975?

108. In which country did Sissons finish his playing days?

109. In 1966 John scored a hat-trick against Leeds, in which competition?

110. Who else scored a hat-trick in the same match?

QUIZ 12
SUBSTITUTES

111. Who was the first player to come on as a sub for West Ham in the league?

112. Who was the first man to be named as a sub in an FA Cup final for West Ham?

113. Who was the first man to come on as a sub in an FA Cup final for West Ham?

114. Who appeared as sub for West Ham in the 1976 European Cup Winners' Cup final?

115. Who was the Hammers named substitute in the 1980 FA Cup final against Arsenal?

116. Which manager named just six subs instead of the permitted seven for a West Ham game at Huddersfield?

117. In the first year substitutes were allowed in league football, 1965/66, West Ham only used a substitute three times, true or false?

118. Who was the first substitute to score a league goal for West Ham?

119. Including the season the first league goal was scored by a sub, how many seasons had passed since the introduction of substitutes?

120. Which of these players made more substitute appearances than starts for West Ham: Franz Carr, John Carroll, Ray Houghton, Paul Kelly, Dave Llewellyn, Dean Martin or Ralph Milne?

FORMER GROUNDS

121. Upton Park was more correctly known as...?

122. The first ever home of Thames Ironworks was played at a ground called XXXXXX Road in Canning Town. Fill in the missing word.

123. A year before Thames Ironworks first played at this ground West Bromwich Albion had played in a very early attempt at a floodlit match against which modern-day Premier League club?

124. What was the less than complimentary name the first ground was nicknamed?

125. The second ground, used briefly to stage home games, was situated under a mile from the Boleyn Ground. Beginning with the letter B it was another XXXX Road. What was it called?

126. Which ground would be the club's third and their home when the name became West Ham United?

127. Which modern day London club were beaten in the first competitive game at the ground?

128. Who beat West Ham in the final game at the ground used prior to the Boleyn Ground?

129. In what year did West Ham move to the Boleyn Ground?

130. In what year did West Ham leave the Boleyn Ground?

1963/64 SEASON

131. Which cup did West Ham win in 1963/64?

132. Which team was beaten in the final?

133. In which other competition did West Ham reach the semi-final?

134. Which local club took the Irons to a replay in the cup West Ham went on to win?

135. Who top scored with 33 goals in all competitions?

136. Who won 8-2 at the Boleyn Ground on Boxing Day only for the Irons to strike back by winning 3-1 at their ground two days later?

137. Who was West Ham's manager?

138. Which club were met in both domestic cups?

139. 39 goals were scored in the two domestic cup competitions, were more scored in the FA Cup or League Cup?

140. Who were the FA Cup holders beaten in the FA Cup semi-final?

JOHN LYALL

141. In which year did John Lyall become manager of West Ham?

142. In 1957 Lyall played alongside Jimmy Greaves at Upton Park for which team?

143. In the same year which cup final did Lyall play in for West Ham?

144. Lyall made his debut for West Ham against Chelsea, in what year?

145. Under Lyall West Ham reached the highest position in the club's history in 1986 - what was the position?

146. Which trophy did West Ham twice win under Lyall?

147. Which manager succeeded Lyall at West Ham?

148. Who did John Lyall manage after leaving the Irons?

149. Which future England midfielder did Lyall sign from non-league Southall?

150. Lyall managed West ham for more games than Billy Bonds played, true or false?

QUIZ 16
FELIPE ANDERSON

151. Which nationality is Felipe?

152. He made his debut as a 17-year-old for which of Pele's old clubs?

153. Who did West Ham sign him from?

154. The fee paid for Anderson was said to be a club record. Was it reported as £26m, £30m or £36m?

155. In 2016 he helped his country win the final of an international tournament against Germany - in what competition?

156. Who did Felipe make his West Ham debut against?

157. When he signed for West Ham Anderson named which South American star as one of three great former West Ham players?

158. How many full international caps did Felipe have when he became West Ham's record signing?

159. In which competition did Anderson score against Dynamo Kiev and RB Salzburg in his last season before coming into English football?

160. How old was Felipe when he signed for West Ham?

MANUEL PELLEGRINI

161. Pellegrini is not the last name of Manuel's full name. What is?

162. In which country did he manage most recently before coming to West Ham?

163. Which other English club has Manuel managed?

164. In which year did he win the Premier League?

165. Which other trophy did his side also win in the year he won the Premier League?

166. Which trophy did Pellegrini win in England in 2015/16?

167. As a player which country did he win 28 caps for?

168. Which country did both of his parents come from?

169. With which Spanish club did he achieve 96 points in 2009/10 without winning the league?

170. How many different countries has Pellegrini won the league title in as a manager?

171. Who was manager of West Ham at the start of the season?

172. Who was manager of West Ham at the end of the season?

173. In which month did the managerial change take place?

174. What position in the Premier League did West Ham finish?

175. Which German team did West Ham play twice in the pre-season Betway Cup?

176. Who did West Ham win 4-1 away to in the Premier League?

177. Who did West Ham beat at Wembley?

178. Which League One side did West Ham knock out of the FA Cup after extra-time in a replay?

179. Which player left to join Mexican club Tigres?

180. Which goalkeeper arrived on loan from Manchester City?

181. Who was appointed as West Ham's new manager before the start of the season?

182. Which German team were beaten on penalties in the Betway Cup?

183. Who scored the Irons' first Premier League Goal of the Season?

184. Which side were beaten away from home in the season's opening domestic cup tie?

185. Which player was signed from Toulouse?

186. Who was the goalkeeper bought from Swansea City?

187. Who was the England international signed after leaving Arsenal?

188. Who was the Senegal international sold to Crystal Palace?

189. Who was the striker loaned to Middlesbrough?

190. Which member of the squad had been signed from a club in Denmark?

QUIZ 20
THE TWENTIES

191. During the 1920s West Ham played in the first-ever Wembley FA Cup final in which year?

192. Who did they play at Wembley?

193. What did West Ham win in that season?

194. Who was West Ham's manager for the entire decade?

195. Which player scored six times in an 8-2 win over Leeds in 1929?

196. Which North London rivals were beaten 7-0 in 1927?

197. Including 1919/20 and 1929/30, how many times did West Ham finish in the top ten of the First Division during the roaring twenties?

198. At which West London ground did West Ham and Arsenal play an FA Cup second replay in 1924/25?

199. In the final full season of the decade, 1928/29 West Ham scored 55 goals in 21 home games. Did they concede more, the same number or fewer in their away games?

200. From January 1920 to the end of the 1922/23 season, did West Ham score four, seven or ten hat-tricks (or better) in league and cup?

QUIZ 21
MARTIN PETERS

201. Peters scored in the 1966 World Cup final but was it England's first, second, third or fourth goal?

202. Was it scored with his right foot, left foot or head?

203. How many of his 67 England caps did he win as a West Ham player: 23, 33 or 43?

204. Who described Peters as being 'Ten years ahead of his time'?

205. How old was Martin when he scored in the World Cup final?

206. In which year did he make his England debut?

207. How many goals did he score in his 67 internationals: Eight, 14 or 20?

208. Who did he score against at the 1970 World Cup?

209. Who did he leave West Ham for shortly before the 1970 World Cup?

210 . Which player came to West Ham in part-exchange for Peters?

211. Joe made his debut against Swansea City
     - in which competition?

212. In what year was that debut?

213. Joe's first Premier League goal came in a 5-4 win
     - against which team?

214. In which year was Cole Hammer of the Year?

215. Which club did Cole join after leaving West Ham?

216. In which year did he play in the Champions League final?

217. Who did he join on a free transfer in 2010?

218. Which French club did he join on loan in 2011?

219. In which year did Joe re-join West Ham?

220. Did Joe win under or over 50 caps for England?

QUIZ 23
THE WHITE HORSE FINAL

221. In which year was 'The White Horse' final?

222. Which competition was it the final of?

223. Which Stadium was it held in?

224. How many previous finals had this stadium staged?

225. Who were West Ham playing?

226. What was the score?

227. Who was the future Middlesbrough manager who scored the first goal of the game?

228. Who was manager of West Ham?

229. What was the name of the final's famous white horse?

230. What was the name of the person riding the horse?

QUIZ 24
ATTENDANCES

231. Who were the opponents in West Ham's record attendance at the Boleyn Ground?

232. In what year was that attendance recorded?

233. Was the record attendance 42,322, 43,322 or 44,322?

234. In 1955 the lowest league attendance at the Boleyn Ground was recorded at 4,373 - against who?

235. A record crowd of 56,996 was recorded against which team on 2 January 2017?

236. Who were West Ham playing when they took part in the game with the biggest attendance ever recorded in England, of over 126,000?

237. What was the occasion of the nation's highest attendance?

238. What was the official attendance of the 1980 FA Cup final between West Ham and Arsenal?

239. The semi-finals of 1975 and 1980 both went to replays. Which of them had the highest aggregate attendance?

240. Which of West Ham's European Cup Winners' Cup finals were watched by the bigger gate, 1965 or 1976?

241. In which year did Lou Macari become manager of West Ham?

242. Who did he sell to Manchester United within a few weeks of taking over?

243. Macari signed Trevor Morley and Ian Bishop from Manchester City with which player going in the opposite direction as part of the deal?

244. Of Italian parents which city was Macari born in?

245. With which club did he win two Scottish league titles?

246. Which club was Macari's first in England?

247. Which club did he win a second division championship medal with in England in 1974?

248. Which was the first club Macari managed?

249. Which goalkeeper was his final signing for West Ham?

250. With which club did he win promotion and the Autoglass Trophy?

DAVID MOYES

251. In which season did Moyes manage West Ham?

252. Which was the first club he managed?

253. Other than the Charity Shield which other trophy has he won as a manager?

254. Up to which age did he represent Scotland?

255. Who did he replace as West Ham manager?

256. Which team did he manage in Spain?

257. Which was the first English club he played for?

258. Did he win more games than he lost as West Ham boss?

259. How many years did he complete of his six-year contract with Manchester United before being sacked?

260. When West Ham beat Huddersfield in January 2018 what landmark did it reach for Moyes?

FRANK McAVENNIE

261. Was Frank born in Glasgow or Edinburgh?

262. Who did West Ham initially sign Frank from?

263. Who did West Ham both sell him to and sign him from?

264. Apart from West Ham which other two clubs did he have two spells with?

265. Which club did he play for on loan?

266. Which club in Northern Ireland did he make one appearance for and score in a semi-final?

267. Which club outside of Europe did be play for?

268. Which Scottish club did he play for without being involved in a transfer to or from West Ham?

269. After leaving West Ham for the final time which English club did he sign for?

270. In which season did Frank win promotion with West Ham?

BRYAN 'POP' ROBSON

271. In what season was Robson top scorer in the First Division?

272. How many goals did he score that season?

273. How many spells did Robson have with West Ham?

274. Who was he signed from the first time he came to West Ham?

275. Who did West Ham sell him to and then sign him from?

276. Robson made a scoring debut for West Ham when he first arrived, against which club?

277. Which other London club did he have a spell for as a veteran?

278. Other than Sunderland where he was briefly caretaker-manager, which northern club did he both play for and manage?

279. What was the highest level Robson represented England at?

280. He scored 47 league goals in each of his spells with West Ham. Did he play more games in his first stint or his second?

281. In which decade did Vic Keeble play for West Ham?

282. With whom had he won an FA Cup winner's medal before joining the Irons?

283. Who did he form a prolific scoring double act with at Upton Park?

284. The manager who signed Keeble for West Ham had previously also signed him for which other club?

285. Who was that manager?

286. In the 80 games he played for West Ham how many goals did he score: 29, 39 or 49?

287. Keeble scored two hat-tricks in his first season with West Ham, one against Stoke in the league and the other against which team in the FA Cup?

288. Who did he score four goals against in a 6-3 win?

289. Before he played in the league which London club had he been associated with?

290. He had to retire through a back injury at what age?

THE THIRTIES

291. Who became manager in 1932 and was still in charge in 1950?

292. He took over from a manager who had been in charge for 30 years. Who was that?

293. What was the furthest West Ham got in the FA Cup during the thirties?

294. On that occasion they lost to which team at Molineux?

295. Which future multiple Champions League winners did West Ham slaughter 7-0 in 1930 to equal the club record victory at the time?

296. Which division did West Ham begin the decade in?

297. And which division were they in when it ended?

298. The highest seasonal goals tally by an individual during the decade was 29, scored in 32 games in 1933/34 by which club legend?

299. In the final season before World War Two which north London side did West Ham meet in the FA Cup at Highbury?

300. What non-footballing qualification did Scottish inside-forward of the thirties Jimmy Marshall have?

ROBERT GREEN

301. Green came to West Ham after 223 league appearances for which club?

302. Did he make the same number, fewer or more league appearances for West Ham?

303. After leaving West Ham, for which club did he then top 100 league appearances?

304. Which were the first northern club he played for?

305. Which club was he on the books of in 2017/18?

306. Which club did he sign for in the summer of 2018?

307. In which season at West Ham did Green save the first three penalties he faced?

308. In which season was Robert voted Hammer of the Year?

309. How many times did he play for England?

310. How many of his England caps were won while with West Ham?

LUDEK MIKLOSKO

311. Which manager signed Ludek for West Ham?

312. Who were the opponents when in his fourth game for West Ham he played in the second leg of a League Cup semi-final?

313. In his first full season Miklosko played all 56 games including 46 in the league. Who was the only other player to start as many as 40 league games?

314. When he was ever-present in the 1992/93 promotion season how many other ever-presents were there in the team?

315. In his last game Miklosko scored an own goal. Who were West Ham playing?

316. Which club did he leave West Ham to join?

317. Who did West Ham sign Miklosko from?

318. His final two international caps were won with the Czech Republic. Who were his first 40 won with?

319. After retiring as a player, in what capacity did Ludek return to West Ham?

320. In which year was Ludek named Hammer of the Year?

QUIZ 33
ERNIE GREGORY

321. What position did Ernie Gregory play?

322. He played over 400 games for West Ham.
How many times was he ever-present
in the league: zero, one or two?

323. Having signed as a professional in 1939, in which season
did Ernie play his first league game for West Ham?

324. In which season did he make his final appearance
for the club?

325. In 1952 Ernie achieved international recognition
for England, at what level?

326. Before signing for West ham which league did
he win with Leytonstone?

327. What role did the LD Alajuelense club of Costa Rica
play in Gregory's career?

328. Having joined the coaching staff after his career, how
many complete decades did Ernie serve West Ham?

329. In what season did he win promotion with the Irons?

330. As a schoolboy which final did he play in
at Upton Park in 1936?

331. What nickname was Byrne known by due
to his talkative nature?

332. He became the first Fourth Division player
to be capped at Under 23 level for England
when he was playing for which London club?

333. Which player was transferred in part exchange
for Byrne when he became West Ham's record buy
as £58,000 also changed hands?

334. Who was the club West Ham signed him from?

335. Who did West Ham sell him to just under five years later?

336. Which other London club did he subsequently sign for?

337. In which country did Byrne complete his career?

338. How many goals did he score for England
in the ten caps he won while with West Ham?

339. Who did he score a hat-trick against for England
as a West Ham player?

340. In which FA Cup winning year was Byrne
Hammer of the Year?

QUIZ 35
MATTHEW UPSON

341. How many different clubs had Matthew played first team football for before joining West Ham?

342. And how many did he play for after he left the Irons?

343. How many of his other clubs did he play as many league games for as he did for West Ham?

344. Who did he make his league debut for?

345. And who did he play his final league match for?

346. Who did West Ham sign Upson from?

347. After his number six shirt was retired in tribute to Bobby Moore, which squad number did he take?

348. Which club did he move on to after leaving West Ham?

349. How many times did he play for England: 21, 31 or 41?

350. Did he win under or over half of his full caps while with West Ham?

QUIZ 36
VALON BEHRAMI

351. Born in Kosovo, which international team did Behrami represent?

352. Which Italian team did West Ham sign him from?

353. Which Italian team did he join from West Ham?

354. In which year did he sign for West Ham?

355. Which other English club did he play for?

356 . Which German team did he play for?

357. He won one trophy in his club career up to 2018 - with which club?

358. Who were West Ham playing when Valon suffered an anterior cruciate ligament injury in 2009?

359. Who were West Ham playing when Behrami made his debut?

360. How many different World Cups did he appear in?

QUIZ 37
SCOTT PARKER

361. In which year did Scott Parker sign for West Ham?

362. When he retained the Hammer of the Year award Parker became the first player to do so since who?

363. How many times did he win the Hammer of the Year in total?

364. In which season was Scott the Football Writers' Association Footballer of the Year?

365. Which was the first club where Parker became Player of the Year?

366. How many full caps did he win for England?

367. How many times was he capped while on West Ham's books?

368. During his career which was the only club Parker played for on loan?

369. Other than his loan, which was the only club outside the capital Scott played for?

370. How many London clubs did Parker represent?

DYLAN TOMBIDES

371. Which shirt number was retired when Dylan passed away?

372. Which country was Dylan from?

373. How old was he when he passed away far too early?

374. Up to what age group had he represented his country?

375. On 22 May 2011 he was named as a substitute at the Boleyn Ground against Sunderland in which competition?

376. On 25 September 2012 Dylan made his debut for West Ham in the League Cup against which team?

377. The charity, the DT38 Foundation was set up to raise awareness of what?

378. Whose Testimonial at Easter 2016 raised money for the DT38 Foundation?

379. Who was Dylan's brother who played as a substitute in that testimonial?

380. Who is the only other player to have his shirt number retired apart from Dylan?

381. Who were Tony's first club?

382. He made 277 league appearances for them. Did he play more or fewer in the colours of West Ham?

383. In which year did Tony join the Irons?

384. In the 1991 FA Cup semi-final Gale became the first man shown a red card for a denying a goalscoring opportunity with a professional foul. Who did he impede?

385. Which former West Ham player scored against Tony's next club Blackburn when he debuted for them at Wembley in the Charity Shield?

386. What was Tony's nickname at West Ham?

387. At what level did Tony represent England?

388. Who were his final Football League club?

389. Which non-league team did he play for between 1996 to 1998?

390. Which non-league side did Gale become chairman of?

QUIZ 40
THE FORTIES

391. Who was manager of West Ham throughout the decade?

392. When the Football League resumed after World War Two the first home game was against: Fulham, Arsenal or Millwall?

393. West Ham won the Football League War Cup in 1940. Where was the final played?

394. Who were beaten 1-0 in the final?

395. In seven war-time seasons between 1939/40 and 1945/46 how many times did West Ham win the league: zero, five or seven?

396. In seven war-time seasons between 1939/40 and 1945/46 how many times did West Ham finish runners-up in the league: zero, five or seven?

397. Which Manchester City and future Derby and Northern Ireland international legend played for West Ham as a 'Guest' player during the war?

398. In 1944 a VI Flying bomb destroyed part of the Boleyn Ground, true or false?

399. As the forties ended which division were West Ham playing in?

400. When the FA Cup restarted after the war Arsenal were beaten 6-0 in the first game. How many goals were scored in the first 20 minutes: zero, four or six?

ANDY MALCOLM

401. In which season was Andy Malcolm a promotion winner with West Ham?

402. In which season did he make his debut?

403. In which season did he play the last of his 300 plus games for the Irons?

404. How many times was he ever-present in all 42 league games: zero, one or two?

405. When he left West Ham which other London club did he move to?

406. Which player signed for West Ham in the move that saw Malcolm move on?

407. Which was Malcolm's third London club?

408. What was the ironic nickname given to Andy because of his serious expression?

409. Which other country did he play in as a veteran?

410. Where did the East Ham-born settle and run a pub after his career was over?

411. In what year did Ilunga come to West Ham?

412. He joined on loan from which club?

413. Who did he replace at left-back following his sale to the same club West Ham had signed him from?

414. Ilunga scored against Barnsley and Middlesbrough, in which competition?

415. Who did he join on loan from West Ham?

416. Which manager sent him on loan?

417. Which of these French clubs did he NOT play for: Saint-Etienne, Toulouse, Rennes, Nantes, Carquefou or Creteil?

418. Which club in Spain was his first in Europe?

419. He played over 100 games for only one of his clubs, which one?

420. Who did he represent at international level in over 30 games?

421. What was Ronnie's nickname, given to him because his work-rate was like clockwork?

422. How old was Boyce when he made his debut for West Ham?

423. What was his most telling contribution to the 1964 FA Cup final against Preston?

424. What was his most telling contribution to the 1964 FA Cup semi-final against holders Manchester United?

425. Did he average over or under one goal for every ten games in his West Ham career?

426. How many times did he play over 50 games in a season for the club in all competitions?

427. In which season did he make his debut?

428. In which season did he make his final appearance for West Ham?

429. At what level did he play internationally?

430. He scored West Ham's first-ever goal in European competition - against who?

YOSSI BENAYOUN

431. Benayoun was born in the month West Ham won the FA Cup, but in which year?

432. In which country was he born?

433. With which famous Dutch team was he part of the youth set-up?

434. Which Spanish club did he join West Ham from?

435. In which year did he join West Ham?

436. Who was the manager who signed him?

437. Having been born in the month West Ham won the FA Cup, in which year's FA Cup final did he play for the Irons?

438. Which club did he join a year after playing against Liverpool in the FA Cup final?

439. He later returned to West Ham, on loan from which club?

440. Did he play over or under 100 full internationals?

AARON CRESSWELL

441. Who did West Ham sign Cresswell from?

442. In which season was he Hammer of the Year?

443. Which club did Aaron begin his career with?

444. Who did he make his England debut against?

445. Who was Aaron's only goal of the 2017/18 season against?

446. Cresswell's previous goal had come two season's earlier, against which club in a 2-2 away draw?

447. His first goal in West Ham colours brought a 1-0 home win over which North-Eastern team in November 2014?

448. In which year did Cresswell make his league debut for his first club?

449. In 2011 he was part of a defence that conceded twelve goals in five days. Who was he playing for at the time?

450. In which city was Aaron born?

451. Javier was born in Guadalajara in Mexico.
Which West Ham player scored defending champions
England's first goal of the 1970 World Cup in that city?

452. Who did Javier score against in the 2018 World Cup
finals as a West Ham player?

453. In which year did Javier join West Ham?

454. Which of his former clubs did Hernandez play against
on his Irons debut?

455. Which club did that former club send Hernandez
on loan to in 2014/15?

456. Which manager was in charge for part of Javier's
time at both of his English clubs?

457. Which German club did West Ham sign him from?

458. What is Javier's nickname?

459. What does that nickname translate as?

460. Who did he score twice against in only his second
game for the Irons?

EYAL BERKOVIC

461. Who were the first English club Berkovic played for?

462. Which international team did he play for?

463. Who was the manager who brought Eyal to Upton Park?

464. Who did he score the winner against in his first game at Upton Park?

465. Which Scottish team did West Ham sell Berkovic to?

466. Returning from Scotland, with which team did he win promotion with?

467. The manager who signed Eyal for West Ham later also signed him for which club?

468. In how many of his first four games for West Ham did Berkovic score?

469. His last goal for West Ham came in a 5-1 win over which team in April 1999?

470. In all competitions Berkovic played 79 games for West Ham, did he score over or under 15 goals?

471. Which famous Tyneside Boys club did Michael begin his career with?

472. In which final did he score twice for West Ham against Coventry in 1999?

473. In which European competition did Carrick make his debut?

474. Who did Michael go on loan to early in his Hammers career?

475. Which was the second club Carrick went on loan to?

476. Which club did he move to in 2004?

477. With which club did Michael make over 300 appearances?

478. Was Carrick capped 34, 44 or 54 times by England?

479. Michael made his England debut as a West Ham player against Mexico at Derby. Which manager gave him his debut?

480. Carrick's last game for West Ham was in the 2004 Play-Off final, against which club?

QUIZ 49
MANUEL LANZINI

481. Which country is Lanzini from?

482. Who were Lanzini's first club?

483. Who did Lanzini score twice against
in a 3-1 win at the end of 2017/18?

484. Who else did he score twice in a game against
in 2017/18?

485. Lanzini marked his West Ham debut against
Astra Giurgiu with a goal, in which competition?

486. Manuel's first Premier League goal came
in a 3-0 win away to which club?

487. In 2016/17 he was runner-up to who
as Hammer of the Year?

488. Who did Lanzini make his full international
debut against?

489. At which English ground did Lanzini score
his first international goal?

490. Which Arabian club did West Ham sign Lanzini from?

491. Who became manager in 1950 and was still in charge at the end of the decade?

492. In which season did West Ham win Division Two?

493. In that season left winger Malcolm Musgrove scored nine goals, how many players scored more?

494. Having been promoted the Irons won their first three games, the third of them by 7-2 - against Aston Villa, Wolves or Newcastle United?

495. Which future England manager lined up in the Hull side that visited West Ham in the opening game of the 1950/51 season?

496. Which famous future manager scored at both ends to beat Brentford in the final of the London Challenge Cup in 1952/53?

497. In January 1954 West Ham came back from 3-0 down to beat which London side who included Jimmy Hill?

498. Who scored a post-war record of 26 goals in 1954/55?

499. Which future Manchester United manager moved from West Ham to Preston in 1956?

500. West Ham scored a record number of league goals in 1957/58. Was it under or over 100?

PHIL PARKES

501. At which club did Phil begin his professional career?

502. From which club did West Ham sign Phil in 1979?

503. Who was the Hammers' manager when Phil joined the club?

504. The £565,000 transfer fee that the Hammers paid for Phil set a new world record for a goalkeeper, true or false?

505. Ironically Phil played his first and last game for the Hammers against the same club. Can you name them?

506. On how many occasions did Phil play for the Hammers at Wembley?

507. Which goalkeeper made more appearances for West Ham, Phil or Robert Green?

508. Against which country did Phil make his full international debut?

509. How many England caps did Phil win during his lengthy playing career?

510. At which club did Phil end his professional career?

511. In which year did John make his first-team debut for West Ham?

512. In what position did John play for the majority of his Hammers' career?

513. During the Hammers' 1957/58 Second Division title-winning season, how many league goals did John score, was it six, seven or eight?

514. John was almost ever-present in the aforementioned 1957/58 campaign. How many league games did he miss, was it one, two or three matches?

515. How many league games did he play for the club: 281, 381 or 481?

516. Other than West Ham, which other league club did John play for?

517. At which club did be begin his managerial career?

518. Can you name John's former Upton Park teammate who became his assistant at Norwich City?

519. In which season did John lead Manchester City to the FA Cup Final?

520. After retiring from playing, but before moving into management, what line of business did John venture into?

CRAIG BELLAMY

521. Born in 1979, where in Wales was Craig's birthplace?

522. With which club did Craig begin his professional career?

523. From which club did the Hammers sign Craig in the summer of 2007?

524. What was the reported transfer fee that West Ham paid for him?

525. Against which club did he make his West Ham debut?

526. Craig's first two West Ham goals came in a League Cup tie, can you name the opposition?

527. In December 2008 Craig was on target in a 1-1 London derby away to which club?

528. In total how many appearances did he make for the Hammers: 26, 28 or 30?

529. When Craig left West Ham in January 2009, which club signed him?

530. Who won more caps for Wales, Craig or James Collins?

JOHN McDOWELL

531. Who was the Hammers' manager that handed John his first-team debut?

532. Can you recall the Upton Park opposition when McDowell made his debut?

533. In which season did John feature in ten League Cup ties for the Hammers?

534. A rare goalscorer, John once netted twice in a Second Division fixture in 1979 as the Hammers walloped which club 5-0 at Upton Park?

535. In total how many goals did John net for the Hammers: five, seven or nine?

536. John was in the West Ham side that suffered an FA Cup third round exit away to which Fourth Division club in 1978/79?

537. How many first team appearances did John make for West Ham: under 300, over 300 or 300 exactly?

538. Which former West Ham defender signed John for Norwich City in the summer of 1979?

539. What was the fee that the Hammers received from the Canaries for John?

540. At which club did John become assistant manager in 1982?

QUIZ 55
TED FENTON

541. In which year did Ted made his debut for the Hammers?

542. On the opening day of the 1935/36 Second Division season, Ted was part of a West Ham side that faced a club playing at their new ground for the very first time. Can you name the venue?

543. The outbreak of World War Two called a halt to Ted's league career with the Hammers. Although he played in many war-time fixtures, how many official league and cup games did he play for the club: 159, 169 or 179?

544. At the end of the war Ted became player/manager at which then Southern League club?

545. When Ted returned to Upton Park as assistant manager in 1948, who was Hammers' boss?

546. In which year did Ted become West Ham United manager?

547. Ted managed the Hammers to the Second Division title in 1957/58, which club did they hold off to land the title?

548. During the 1957/58 title success, Fenton's team scored over 100 league goals, true or false?

549. Who succeeded Ted as Hammers' manager?

550. After West Ham, which was the next club that Ted took charge of?

551. Alan was born in Middlesex on 13 April, but in what year?

552. Which London club twice rejected Alan before he began a career in non-league football?

553. At which non-league club was Alan plying his trade when he was spotted by the Hammers in 1976?

554. Often referred to as West Ham's 'best-ever buy', what fee did the Hammers pay for him?

555. Alan made his Hammers' debut in a League Cup tie at home to which London rival in October 1976?

556. In which season did Alan register his best return of league goals for the club?

557. In that mystery season how many league goals did he score: five, six or seven?

558. At which venue did Alan score the opening goal in the 1980 FA Cup semi-final replay victory over Everton?

559. Which shirt number did Alan wear in the Hammers' 1980 FA Cup final victory over Arsenal?

560. Other than West Ham, can you name the only other league club Alan has played for?

561. At which club did Keith begin his career, progressing though the youth ranks and going on to make 14 league appearances?

562. In which year did Keith join the Hammers?

563. Who was the Hammers' boss that handed Keith his debut for the club?

564. Can you recall the transfer fee West Ham paid for Keith: £60,000, £160,000 or £260,000?

565. His West Ham debut came in a League Cup tie as the Hammers cruised to a 6-0 victory at Upton Park. Can you recall the opposition?

566. Keith marked his league debut with a goal as the Hammers scored six goals in consecutive home games. Can you name the opposition?

567. Keith scored for West Ham in the 1976 European Cup Winners' Cup final defeat to Anderlecht, what did his goal make the score at the time?

568. Who played more league games for the Hammers, Keith or Stewart Robson?

569. Before leaving West Ham Keith spent a period on loan with Team Hawaii in the North American Soccer League, true or false?

570. Can you name the Welsh club that Keith joined after leaving Upton Park?

571. In which season was the Hammer of the Year
first presented?

572. Who currently decides the winner of the trophy?

573. Can you name the first-ever recipient of the award?

574. In which season did a runner-up also
become announced?

575. Who was the first goalkeeper to win the award?

576. In which season was Bobby Moore first voted
Hammer of the Year?

577. Can you name the winner of the award during
the club's 1979/80 FA Cup winning season?

578. In which season was Joe Cole voted
Hammer of the Year?

579. On how many occasions has Mark Noble been
presented with the award?

580. Who was the last English player to land the award?

LIAM BRADY

581. At which London club did Liam begin his career?

582. With which country did he win 72 international caps?

583. In which country was Liam playing his club football prior to joining West Ham United?

584. In what season did Liam join the Hammers?

585. Against which 'City' did Liam make his West Ham debut: Norwich, Manchester or Leicester?

586. How many goals did Liam total in his Upton Park career? Was it more than ten, under ten or ten goals exactly?

587. Liam was on target in his final game for the Hammers in May 1990. Can you name the opposition?

588. During his West Ham career how many permanent managers did Liam play under?

589. Which Scottish club did he manage in the early 1990s?

590. Liam has managed one English league club, can you name them?

THE 1960s

591. Which manager began a long and successful reign as West Ham boss in April 1961?

592. The Hammers won the FA Cup in 1964. What stage of the competition did they reach in the previous season?

593. Can you name the club's leading scorer from the 1963/64 season?

594. The club's highest league finish in the 1960s was eighth in the First Division. In which two seasons did they achieve this?

595. In February 1967 which long-serving defender played his final game for the club?

596. During the 1960s, how many times was Geoff Hurst voted Hammer of the Year?

597. Which club legend broke through to the first team in the 1967/68 season?

598. Against which club did the Hammers suffer a League Cup semi-final defeat in 1966/67?

599. Which future West Ham goalscoring sensation was born in Glasgow in November 1960?

600. West Ham said goodbye to the swinging sixties with a 1-1 draw at Upton Park on 27 December 1969. Can you name the opposition?

QUIZ 61
TREVOR MORLEY

601. After starting out in non-league football, with which club did Trevor turn professional in 1985?

602. Trevor was transferred to Manchester City in 1988, while at Maine Road he scored the goal that secured City promotion from the Second Division on the final day of the 1988/89 season away to Bradford City, true or false?

603. Which Manchester City manager saw no place for Trevor in his plans and sold him to West Ham?

604. Against which club did Trevor make his Hammers' debut?

605. He netted his first West Ham goal against which team?

606. Trevor topped the Hammers' scoring charts in the 1990/91 promotion-winning season. How many goals did he net in all competitions: 17, 18 or 19 goals?

607. Trevor scored 70 goals throughout this West Ham career, how many were top-flight league goals?

608. Trevor was sent off once in his West Ham career, in which competition did he see red in at Upton Park in 1992?

609. Does Trevor's 70-goal haul for the Hammers see him sit above or below John Sissons in the club's goalscoring charts?

610. In which season was Trevor voted Hammer of the Year?

QUIZ 62
JUST THE ONCE

611. Whose only goal for West Ham happened to also be the club's very first Premier League goal?

612. Can you name the former Hammer who marked his debut with his only goal for the club in a 4-1 defeat away to Everton in 1960?

613. Speedy winger Franz Carr featured in three games for the Hammers but started just one during a month on loan from Nottingham Forest in March 1991, true or false?

614. Who made his one and only appearance for the Hammers as a late substitute in a 4-2 victory over Crewe Alexandra in March 2004?

615. Whose only goal for the Hammers secured a 1-1 draw away to Leeds United in March 2012?

616. Can you name the opposition when Kyel Reid scored his only goal for the club in a League Cup tie in 2008?

617. Which defender who amassed almost 100 games for the Hammers scored his only goal in a 1-1 draw away to Newcastle United in November 1996?

618. Whose one and only appearance for the Hammers came in a League Cup tie at Burnley in October 2013?

619. Long-serving defender Steve Potts may have played over 500 games for the Hammers but he scored just once. Against which club did he make his solo strike?

620. On loan Austrian defender Emanuel Pogatetz made just one league start in the 2012/13 Premier League season, who was it against: Swansea City, Aston Villa or Stoke City?

621. Who were the opposition that the Hammers shared six goals with on Boxing Day 2017?

622. West Ham turned on the style to win 4-1 away at which Premier League club in 2016?

623. During the 1985/86 season the Hammers suffered a London derby defeat on Boxing Day. Who was it against?

624. On Boxing Day 1987 who did the Hammers welcome to Upton Park for a London derby fixture?

625. Boxing Day 1989 took the Hammers to East Anglia but who did they face: Norwich City or Ipswich Town?

626. What was the score when West Ham hosted Oldham Athletic in a top-of-the-table clash on Boxing Day 1990?

627. Who provided the Hammers' first Premier League opposition on Boxing Day?

628. The Hammers won their first Boxing Day Premier League match against Coventry City in 1997. Who scored the only goal of the game?

629. In the FA Cup winning season of 1974/75, who was on target for the Hammers in their 1-1 Boxing Day draw with Tottenham Hotspur at Upton Park?

630. The Hammers have yet to host a game at the new London Stadium on a Boxing Day, true or false?

631. The Hammers won the cup in 1964 by using the same eleven players in each round of the competition, true or false?

632. The third round draw handed West Ham a London derby at home to which club?

633. Who netted a brace in the fourth round replay at home to Leyton Orient?

634. Geoff Hurst scored twice in the 3-1 win at Swindon in the fifth round but who got the other West Ham goal?

635. Who did the Hammers defeat in the quarter-final?

636. Manchester United provided the Hammers' semi-final opponents. United were cup holders at the time, true or false?

637. A week before the semi-final, the two sides met in the First Division at Upton Park. What was the score in the league match?

638. On which ground did the Hammers defeat Manchester United 3-1 in the semi-final?

639. Who lined up for Preston in the final and in doing so became the youngest player to play in an FA Cup final?

640. In which minute of the final did Ronnie Boyce score the Hammers' winning goal?

1965 EUROPEAN CUP WINNERS' CUP

641. Which trophy did the Hammers win in 1964 to qualify for the 1964/65 European Cup Winners' Cup competition?

642. Who scored the Hammers' first goal in the competition?

643. In which fixture was that first goal of the campaign scored?

644. What was the aggregate score of West Ham's second round tie with Sparta Prague?

645. Can you recall the Hammers' quarter-final opponents?

646. Who netted a brace for the Hammers in the second leg of the quarter-final at Upton Park?

647. What was the attendance for the semi-final first leg at home to Real Zaragoza, was it over or under 35,000?

648. Who did the Hammers face in the final?

649. Which venue hosted the final?

650. Who scored both goals to give the Hammers a 2-0 victory in the final?

HAMMERS AT THE WORLD CUP

651. West Ham and which two other clubs had three players in England's 1966 World Cup squad?

652. Of the West Ham trio of Bobby Moore, Martin Peters and Geoff Hurst - who was the oldest?

653. Only Bobby Moore and Martin Peters started England's opening game in 1966 v Uruguay, true or false?

654. Famed for his World Cup final hat-trick, how many goals did Geoff Hurst total in the competition?

655. In what minute of the final did Martin Peters score to put England in front for the first time?

656. All three Hammers heroes of '66 began their careers at Upton Park, true or false?

657. How many West Ham players were named in England's World Cup squad for Mexico in 1970?

658. Who was the single Hammer named in Ron Greenwood's England squad for the World Cup finals in Spain in 1982?

659. Against which country did Alvin Martin make his only World Cup finals appearance during Mexico '86?

660. Hammers' defender Rio Ferdinand was the youngest member of England's World Cup squad for France 1998, true or false?

661. Which USA international midfielder played for the Hammers during the 1995/96 season?

662. How many international goals did Trevor Brooking score for England?

663. Former Hammers' goalkeeper Ludek Miklosko won international recognition with both Czechoslovakia and the Czech Republic, true or false?

664. Which Croatian international striker was signed from Arsenal in 2000 but failed to have a major impact at West Ham?

665. For which country did former West Ham midfielder Nolberto Solano make over 80 international appearances?

666. Can you name the defender who was voted Hammer of the Year in 2006 and played internationally for Wales?

667. Which Italian defender was a runner-up at Euro 2012 and moved from Juventus to West Ham in 2015?

668. Striker Diafra Sakho played international football for which nation during his time at West Ham?

669. Which Barcelona superstar was on the scoresheet when Upton Park hosted an international friendly between Argentina and Croatia in November 2014?

670. Which former West Ham favourite also featured in that match and received a hero's welcome when he replaced Sergio Aguero after 63 minutes?

OPENING DAY FIXTURES

671. Who took charge of the Hammers for the first time when they began their 2018/19 Premier League campaign away to Liverpool?

672. When did West Ham last win an opening day league fixture?

673. After winning promotion the previous season, West Ham began the 2005/06 season with a 3-1 win at home to Blackburn Rovers. Who scored the Hammers' first goal in that victory?

674. West Ham began their 1979/80 FA Cup winning season with a Second Division fixture away to which Welsh club?

675. Who scored the Hammers' first goal of 2016/17 when they suffered a narrow 2-1 defeat at Chelsea?

676. At which venue did new boss Lou Macari begin his reign with a 1-1 draw on the opening day of the 1989/90 season?

677. Can you name the Hammers' striker who netted an opening day brace to seal a 2-1 home win over Wigan Athletic in 2008?

678. Who scored the winning goal to seal a 2-1 opening day success away to Preston North End in 2003?

679. With Ron Greenwood in charge, who did the Hammers face on the opening day of the 1961/62 season?

680. The Hammers made a flying start to their 1978/79 Second Division campaign. Who was on the receiving end of a 5-2 opening day defeat at Upton Park?

REPRESENTATIVE GAMES AT THE BOLEYN

681. Lionel Messi played for Argentina at the Boleyn Ground in October of which year?

682. Who were Argentina playing?

683. Did Messi score?

684. Carlos Tevez and which other former Hammer played for Argentina on that occasion?

685. Which player with a West Ham connection played against England at the Boleyn Ground in 2003?

686. David James, Rio Ferdinand, Frank Lampard junior, Kieron Dyer and which other player with an Irons connection played for England in that game?

687. In 2012 who did David Haye beat in a Boxing match at the Boleyn Ground?

688. Which team played in three of the five FA Amateur Cup finals held at the Boleyn Ground during the 1930s?

689. Who scored the only goal of the game from the penalty spot as England Under 21s beat Bulgaria Under 21s at West Ham in 1998?

690. Who did England youths score seven against at the Boleyn Ground in 1957?

691. Who scored West Ham's first goal of the 1970s in an FA Cup third round tie away to Middlesbrough on 3 January 1970?

692. The Hammers survived in the top flight in 1970/71 with a 20th-placed finish, which two clubs finished below them and were relegated to the Second Division?

693. West Ham's best league finish in the 1970s occurred in 1972/73. In which position in the First Division table did the club finish?

694. Which club did the Hammers play in a top-flight fixture for the first time in 1972/73?

695. The Hammers suffered relegation from the First Division in 1977/78. For how many seasons were they outside the top flight?

696. Which member of the Hammers' 2004/05 Play-Off winning side was born in Bellshill, Scotland in February 1972?

697. Can you name the West Ham legend who played his final game for the club in a goalless draw with Ipswich Town at Upton Park in March 1970?

698. Against which club did the Hammers suffer a League Cup semi-final defeat 1971/72?

699. On which ground did that defeat occur following a second replay?

700. Which future West Ham manager began his playing career at nearby Leyton Orient in 1973?

JOHN HARTSON

701. In which Welsh city was John born in April 1975?

702. With which club did John begin his professional career?

703. What new record did John's transfer to Arsenal create in January 1995?

704. Who was the Arsenal manager that signed him?

705. After joining the Hammers in February 1997, against which club did he makes his Hammers debut?

706. West Ham were languishing in 18th place in the Premier League table when John arrived, in what position did they end the 1996/97 campaign?

707. In just eleven matches for the Hammers in 1996/97, how many goals did John score to help the club beat the drop?

708. Against which club did John score his only hat-trick for the Hammers?

709. In his 51 games for Wales did John score 7, 14 or 21 goals?

710. After leaving Upton Park, how many British clubs did John play for before retiring and beginning his successful media career?

711. In which season did the Hammers reach their first League Cup final?

712. The Hammers' first appearance in the final resulted in a 5-3 aggregate defeat to which Midlands club?

713. En route to their second League Cup final in 1980/81, how many London sides did the Hammers knock out?

714. Trailing 3-2 from the first leg of their semi-final against Coventry City in 1981, who were the Hammers' second leg goalscorers in a 2-0 win at Upton Park that sent the club to Wembley?

715. Can you name the future West Ham goalkeeper who played in goal for Coventry in that semi-final?

716. Can you name the referee who allowed a controversial goal for Liverpool to stand with just two minutes of extra-time remaining in the final?

717. Who saved the day with a last-minute penalty to take the 1981 final to a replay?

718. At which venue was the replay held?

719. Who scored to give the Hammers an early lead in the replay before Liverpool ran out 2-1 winners?

720. In which season did the Hammers suffer a 6-3 aggregate semi-final defeat to Oldham Athletic?

721. In which soccer-mad city was Mark born in 1962?

722. At which club did Mark begin his career and turn professional but fail to play for the first team?

723. While playing non-league football for Northwich Victoria, Mark was also employed as a: butcher, baker or builder?

724. In which competition did Mark appear in a Wembley final for Northwich Victoria?

725. With which club did Mark finally make his Football League debut?

726. When Mark joined West Ham in the summer of 1985, which player was he signed to replace?

727. What was the transfer fee that the Hammers paid for Mark?

728. Mark was ever-present during his First Division debut season with West Ham, true or false?

729. Mark left West Ham and joined Manchester City in December 1990, which two players moved in the opposite direction as part of that transfer?

730. Can you name the manager who twice signed Mark - once for Manchester City and then for Everton?

731. Alvin featured for the Hammers in the 1975 FA Youth Cup final. Can you recall the opposition: Norwich City, Luton Town or Ipswich Town?

732. Alvin made his Hammers' first-team debut in March 1978. Who were the opposition?

733. Which shirt number did Alvin wear in the 1980 FA Cup final triumph?

734. In only his third game for the club, Alvin scored his first West Ham goal. Who was it against: Leicester City, Liverpool or Leeds United?

735. Alvin made all of his England appearances while with West Ham. How many international caps did he win: 17, 18 or 19?

736. In which World Cup finals was Alvin a member of the England squad?

737. In April 1986 Alvin scored a hat-trick during the Hammers' 8-1 demolition of Newcastle United at Upton Park. Bizarrely he scored against three different Newcastle 'keepers. Can you name all three?

738. After making 596 appearances in all competitions for West Ham, where does Alvin sit in the club's list of all-time appearance makers?

739. Against which club did Alvin make his final appearance for the Hammers in May 1996?

740. At which club did Alvin have a two-year spell as manager?

FA CUP WINNERS 1975

741. Who were the Hammers' third round opponents during their successful 1974/75 FA Cup campaign?

742. West Ham progressed to the fifth round following a fourth round replay victory away to Swindon Town. Can you name the Hammers' two goalscorers from the replay at the County Ground?

743. The fifth round draw handed West Ham a London derby, who were the visitors to Upton Park?

744. Who was the Hammers' two-goal hero in the quarter-final victory over Arsenal at Highbury?

745. Which venue was chosen to host the Hammers' semi-final with Ipswich Town?

746. Ipswich and West Ham could not be separated in the semi-final and a replay was necessary. What was the score from the first meeting?

747. At which ground was the semi-final replay held?

748. The Hammers' quarter-final victory at Arsenal attracted a bigger crowd than the semi-final replay, true or false?

749. Who did the Hammers face in the final?

750. West Ham won the cup thanks to two goals from Alan Taylor in the final. How many goals did Taylor score in total during the cup run?

751. In which country did the Hammers begin their ECWC campaign when they faced Lahden Reipas?

752. What was the aggregate score that West Ham won the first round matches with Lahden Reipas: 5-1, 5-2 or 5-3?

753. From which country were the Hammers' second round opponents Ararat Erevan?

754. With manager John Lyall absent with flu from the third round first leg match away to Den Haag, who took charge of the Hammers?

755. Can you name the Dutch international who netted a 26th minute hat-trick as the home side led the first leg 4-0 at half-time?

756. Who struck twice in the second half for the Hammers to keep the tie alive ahead of the second leg at Upton Park?

757. A 3-1 win in the second leg took John Lyall's men though to the semi-final on the away goals rule after the tie ended 4-4 on aggregate. Who netted the Hammers' opening goal in the second leg?

758. Who were the Hammers' semi-final opponents?

759. Which venue hosted the final against Anderlecht?

760. What was the score in the final?

QUIZ 77
JULIAN DICKS

761. Julian arrived at West Ham from Birmingham City, what fee did the Hammers pay Birmingham for him?

762. In which position did Julian play?

763. He developed a 'hard man' reputation. How many reds cards did he receive while playing for the Hammers: five, seven or nine?

764. Dicks scored his first goal for the Hammers in a London derby, can you name the opposition?

765. How many promotions did Julian help achieve with the Hammers?

766. He was first handed the captain's armband for a match against his former club Birmingham City in 1989, true or false?

767. How many appearances did Julian make for the Hammers: 326, 336 or 346?

768. During his entire playing career, Julian never made an appearance as a substitute, true or false?

769. When Julian joined Liverpool in 1993, which two players came from Anfield to Upton Park as part of the deal?

770. On how many occasions did the fans vote Julian Hammer of the Year?

QUIZ 78
DIMITRI PAYET

771. What nationality is Dimitri?

772. From which club was he signed?

773. Who was the West Ham manager that signed him?

774. Against which club did he make his Premier League debut?

775. Dimitri scored his first goal for West Ham in a match at home to which Premier League side?

776. Against which club did he score both goals in a 2-0 victory at Upton Park in September 2015?

777. After injury resulted in a spell on the sidelines, Payet marked his return to the side with a stunning free-kick against which club in January 2016?

778. How many goals did he score in the 5-1 FA Cup fifth round romp at Blackburn Rovers?

779. He ended the 2015/16 season as Hammer of the Year, can you recall who came second in the fans' end-of-season poll?

780. What fee did the Hammers receive when they sold Payet to Marseille in January 2017?

781. At which club did Dean begin his career?

782. From which club did the Hammers sign Dean in January 2006?

783. Who was the West Ham manager when Dean joined the club?

784. How many goals did Dean score in the Hammers' 2006 FA Cup campaign?

785. Dean made his West Ham debut in a thrilling 3-2 London derby victory away to which club?

786. Against which club did Dean score his first goal for the Hammers?

787. Dean won one full England cap as a West Ham player, can you name the country it came against?

788. Dean scored the second goal in the 2006 FA Cup final to put the Hammers 2-0 up, can you name the Liverpool 'keeper he scored past?

789. In total how many goals did Dean score for the Hammers: 19, 20 or 21?

790. What is fondly remembered about Dean's appearance in Mark Noble's testimonial match at Upton Park in 2016?

FA CUP WINNERS 1980

791. When West Ham won the FA Cup in 1980 they became the last side outside of the top flight to lift the trophy, true or false?

792. In which division were the Hammers playing their league fixtures in 1979/80?

793. Who were West Ham's third round opponents?

794. East London neighbours Orient provided the Hammers' fourth round opposition. What was the score?

795. The Hammers faced Welsh opposition in the fifth round. Who were the visitors to Upton Park: Wrexham, Swansea City or Newport County?

796. Who netted the only goal of the game to see off Aston Villa in the quarter-final at Upton Park?

797. At which venue was the initial semi-final match against Everton hosted?

798. Can you name the West Ham player who scored the winning goal in the semi-final replay?

799. In which minute of the final did Trevor Brooking score the winning goal?

800. Can you name the referee that took charge of the final?

THE EIGHTIES

801. When the Hammers won the Second Division title in 1980/81, which two other clubs were also promoted?

802. The 1981/82 season saw the introduction of three points for a win. How many points did the Hammers amass in the First Division that season: 57, 58 or 59?

803. Which club did the Hammers thrash 5-1 at Upton Park in the penultimate home game of the 1985/86 season?

804. Can you name the West Ham player who was crowned Hammer of the Year on three occasions in the 1980s?

805. Which club legend played his final game for the club in May 1985 at home to Liverpool?

806. Who was the only ever-present player in the 1987/88 First Division campaign?

807. Julian Dicks joined the club in March 1988, from which club was he signed?

808. Which defender joined West Ham from Norwich City in 1983 for a fee of £160,000?

809. When the Hammers suffered relegation in 1988/89, which other two clubs went down with them?

810. Who did the Hammers face in 1989 League Cup semi-final?

DAVID CROSS

811. A which club did David begin his career?

812. Which club did David help to secure a first-ever promotion to the top flight in 1971/72?

813. From which club did the Hammers sign David?

814. West Ham set a new club record for a transfer fee paid when they landed David, how much did he cost?

815. David made his Hammers' debut against the club he had just left, true or false?

816. David was the club's leading goalscorer in the 1980/81 Second Division title-winning season. How many league goals did he score that season: 22, 24 or 26?

817. What club record did David set when he played against Castilla in a European Cup Winners' Cup match in 1980?

818. Who scored more goals for the Hammers, David or Paul Goddard?

819. In 1981/82 David scored all four goals in a 4-0 First Division victory away to which London rival?

820. Which club did David join when he left West Ham in 1982?

SAM ALLARDYCE

821. At which club did Sam make over 200 appearances as a player and later return as manager?

822. With which club was Sam previously in charge before taking over at West Ham?

823. What was Sam's simple brief ahead of his first season at Upton Park?

824. Can you name the defender Sam signed, initially on loan, from Sunderland ahead of the 2011/12 season?

825. In Sam's first competitive match in charge, West Ham lost their opening game of the 2011/12 season to Cardiff City, who was the former Hammer managing the Bluebirds that day?

826. Can you name the West Ham player who scored the first goal of the Allardyce era?

827. After finishing third in the Championship, Sam guided the Hammers to promotion via the play-offs in 2011/12. Which two clubs won automatic promotion that season?

828. Back in the Premier League, which position did Sam guide the Hammers to finish in during the 2012/13 campaign?

829. In February 2014, Sam was named the Premier League Manager of the Month after the Hammers enjoyed five wins from their five league fixtures, true or false?

830. Sam left West Ham at the end of the 2014/15 campaign - in which position did they finish the Premier League that season?

831. Which London club was Jermain playing for prior to joining the Hammers as a 16-year-old?

832. Who were the opposition when Jermain made his first-team debut for the Hammers?

833. Defoe marked his West Ham debut with a goal, true or false?

834. At which club did Jermain score ten goals in consecutive matches while on loan in the 2000/01 season?

835. Against which club did Jermain score his first Premier League goal for the Hammers?

836. What action did Jermain take at the end of the 2002/03 season that drew him criticism from the Hammers' fans?

837. In total how many goals did Jermain score in his West Ham career: 31, 41 or 51?

838. Which club did he play for in between his two spells at Tottenham Hotspur?

839. Jermain made his full England debut in 2004, can you recall the opposition?

840. Which Major Soccer League club did Jermain sign for in 2014?

KEN BROWN

841. In which position did Ken play for Hammers during his 14-year playing career at Upton Park?

842. With which local Dagenham side was Ken playing when he was first spotted by West Ham?

843. In total how many appearances did Ken make for West Ham: 474, 484 or 494?

844. Ken was only the second player to win the Hammer of the Year award, true or false?

845. In November 1959, Ken won his one and only full international cap. Which country was he playing for?

846. Can you name the future Hammers' star who made his first appearance for the club in Ken's testimonial match in May 1967?

847. When Ken became manager of Norwich City, which former West Ham teammate did he take over from?

848. What was the first name of Ken's son who also later played first-team football for the Hammers?

849. As a manger which trophy did Ken lead Norwich City to in 1985?

850. In 2018 which West Ham United honour was bestowed upon Ken?

851. In what position did the Hammers end their 1985/86 First Division campaign?

852. How many points were West Ham shy of champions Liverpool at the end of the season?

853. Who ended the season as the club's leading scorer?

854. The combined strike force of Tony Cottee and Frank McAvennie contributed how many league goals in 1985/86: 44, 45 or 46?

855. On which venue did the Hammers begin the season with a 1-0 opening day defeat?

856. West Ham enjoyed a memorable 2-0 FA Cup fifth round replay victory over Manchester United at Old Trafford in March 1986, can you name the club's two goalscorers?

857. Which club eventually knocked the Hammers out of the FA Cup at the quarter-final stage in 1985/86?

858. In April 1986, which club were thrashed 8-1 by the Hammers in a First Division match at Upton Park?

859. How many points had the Hammers amassed by the end of the season?

860. Who ended the season by collecting the Hammer of the Year award?

MARK NOBLE

861. Prior to joining the Hammers' Academy, which professional club did Mark join as an 11-year-old?

862. Mark set a new record as being the youngest player to feature in a West Ham reserve side. How old was he when he made his debut for the second string?

863. Against which club did Mark make his first-team debut for the Hammers?

864. In which competition were the Hammers competing when Mark made his debut?

865. His league debut came in a Championship match in 2005, can you name the venue?

866. Mark began the 2006/07 season with a loan spell at which club?

867. Against which club did Mark score his first goal for the Hammers?

868. An ace penalty taker, against which club did Mark convert his first West Ham penalty?

869. In April 2016 he scored two penalties in one game as the Hammers defeated which club 3-1 at Upton Park?

870 . Mark holds the record for making the most Premier League appearances for the club, true or false?

RIO FERDINAND

871. Rio was born in Peckham but in which year?

872. What is Rio's middle name: Guy, Gavin or Gareth?

872. Which Hammers' legend did he replace when he made his debut as a substitute on 5 May 1996?

874. Who were West Ham playing when Rio made his debut?

875. Against which club did Rio score his first goal for the Hammers?

876. Which player first broke through to the West Ham first team, Rio or Frank Lampard junior?

877. In which season was Rio voted Hammer of the Year?

878. Against which club did Rio play his final game for West Ham?

879. How many Premier League titles did Rio win while with Manchester United?

880. Who played more games for the Hammers, Rio or his brother Anton?

ANDY CARROLL

881. In which town was Andy born in 1989?

882. Andy began his career at Newcastle United but which club did the Magpies loan him to in 2007/08?

883. From which club did Andy join the Hammers?

884. How many goals did Andy score during his first season at West Ham when initially on loan?

885. Against which club did he score his first goal at Upton Park?

886. What was the reported transfer fee when the Hammers converted Andy's loan to a permanent move?

887. Which season has been Andy's most productive in terms of goals scored since joining the Hammers?

888. Since Andy has been at West Ham, how many permanent managers has the club had?

889. Ahead of the 2018/19 season, all of the 33 goals that Andy had scored for West Ham came in the Premier League, true or false?

890. Against which country did Andy win his first full England cap?

891. Can you name the Hammers' defender who was controversially sent off in the 1991 FA Cup semi-final against Nottingham Forest?

892. On which neutral ground did that fixture take place?

893. In February 1990, which former player took charge of the first team for one match following the resignation of Lou Macari?

894. Can you name the legendary Arsenal striker who joined the Hammers in July 1998?

895. January 1990 saw the Hammers suffer an FA Cup third round exit at the hands of which Fourth Division club?

896. Striker Paul Kitson marked his home debut in February 1997 with a goal in a London derby victory over which club?

897. Despite the team suffering relegation in 1991/92, manager Billy Bonds remained in charge for the 1992/93 season, true or false?

898. In which position in the Premier League did the Hammers finish in 1998/99?

899. Can you name the Welsh striker who ended the 1997/98 season as the club's top scorer?

900. Which club did the Hammers face in their final fixture in the calendar year of 1999?

THE 1990/91 SEASON

901. Can you name the manager that led the Hammers to promotion from the Second Division in 1990/91?

902. The season began with a goalless draw away to which club?

903. Remarkably the Hammers remained unbeaten in the league until December, can you name the first side they suffered a defeat to in 1990/91?

904. One player was ever-present throughout the league campaign, can you name him?

905. Who ended the season as the club's leading league goalscorer?

906. How many goals did our top league scorer net en route to promotion: 12, 14 or 16 goals?

907. Which club did West Ham defeat 2-0 at Upton Park to secure promotion?

908. Promotion was secured with how many league fixtures remaining?

909. Which club pipped the Hammers to the Second Division title on the final day of the season?

910. Can you name the Hammer of the Year from this promotion-winning campaign?

QUIZ 92
PAUL INCE

911. As a youngster Paul was an Arsenal supporter, true or false?

912. In which competition did he make his West Ham debut in November 1986?

913. Against which team did Paul make his First Division debut for the Hammers?

914. How many appearances did Paul make for the Hammers: over 100, under 100 or 100 exactly?

915. In which season did Paul contribute eight goals from the West Ham midfield?

916. Against which club did Paul score two stunning goals in a 4-1 League Cup victory at Upton Park in November 1988?

917. When Paul left West Ham in 1989 which club did he join?

918. Paul won over 50 caps for England but can you name the opposition when he made his international debut?

919. Which Serie A side did Paul play for during a two-year period between 1995 and 1997?

920. At which club has Paul twice served as manager?

THE 1992/93 SEASON

921. Who did manager Billy Bonds appoint as his new assistant ahead of the 1992/93 season?

922. The Hammers began the season with a 1-0 win at Barnsley. Can you recall who scored the first goal of the season?

923. During the 1992/93 season, two outfield players were ever-present. Can you name them both?

924. Who kept goal for the Hammers throughout this promotion-winning season?

925. Clive Allen ended the season as top scorer, true or false?

926. Can you name the Scottish international striker who joined the Hammers on loan from Southampton during 1992/93 and scored four goals in eleven appearances?

927. Which Third Division club knocked the Hammers out of the League Cup in 1992/93?

928. Against which side did the Hammers secure promotion on the final day of the season?

929. West Ham ended the season as runners-up, but which club won the title?

930. Which club ended the season in third place but missed out on promotion due to an inferior goal difference to West Ham?

THE 1993/94 SEASON

931. The 1993/94 season was the first time that the Hammers had competed in the newly formed Premier League, true or false?

932. Which summer signing arrived from Oxford United for a fee of £1.2M?

933. Against which club did the Hammers record their first win of the season?

934. Can you name the striker who marked his debut with a goal in the 2-0 win at Blackburn in September 1993?

935. During this season the Hammers signed midfielder Mike Marsh from which Premier League rival?

936. Against which club did the Hammers share six goals at Upton Park in a thrilling match in January 1994?

937. How many points did West Ham win against champions Manchester United in 1993/94?

938. In which position did the Hammers end the season?

939. Forward Trevor Morley ended the season as top scorer, how many goals did he net in all competitions: 14, 15 or 16?

940. Against which club did West Ham record their final home win of the season?

RAY STEWART

941. With which Scottish club did Ray begin
his professional career?

942. Still aged just 16, Ray's debut saw him handed the
unenviable task of marking which Celtic great?

943. Which award did Ray land at the end of the 1978/79
season before joining West Ham?

944. What fee did the Hammers pay when they
signed Ray in 1979?

945. When Ray joined the Hammers he became
the most expensive teenage footballer in Britain
at the time, true or false?

946. Who was the manager who signed him for West Ham?

947. As a defender Ray scored an incredible 84 goals
for West Ham but how many were direct
from the penalty spot: 74, 76 or 78?

948. What was unique about Ray's place in the 1980
FA Cup final team?

949. What nickname did the West Ham fans give to Ray?

950. When Ray left West Ham in 1992 he returned north
of the border but which club did he join?

951. Who took charge of West Ham for the first time when they faced FC Lusitans in a Europa League qualifying fixture?

952. In that game against FC Lusitans, who made his debut to became the club's youngest player?

953. Opposition FC Lusitans were from which country?

954. West Ham won the match 3-0 against FC Lusitans, can you name the player who opened the scoring?

955. It took a penalty shoot-out for West Ham to knock out Maltese club Birkirkara from the competition in 2015, true or false?

956. Can you name the Romanian side that knocked the Hammers out of the Europa League at the third qualifying round in 2015?

957. How did Mauro Zarate write his name into the Hammers' history books during the 2015/16 Europa League qualifying campaign?

958. What was memorable about the Hammers' Europa League qualifying victory over Domzale on 4 August 2016?

959. Can you name the midfielder who netted twice in the 3-0 victory at home to Domzale?

960. The Hammers' 3-0 second leg win against Domzale saw them progress to the next round on aggregate, but what was the score in the first leg of the tie?

961. Where was Tony born: Barking, Forest Gate or Peckham?

962. How old was Tony when he marked his first-team debut with a goal on New Year's Day 1983?

963. Against which club did Tony score his first Hammers' goal?

964. With which strike partner did Tony form a formidable partnership in the mid-1980s?

965. Tony had two spells with the Hammers, which club did he play for in between?

966. When Tony left Upton Park in 1988 he was briefly the most expensive player to be signed by a British club. What fee did the Hammers receive for him?

967. At the end of which season was Tony voted the PFA Young Player of the Year?

968. In September 1986, Tony scored his first league hat-trick for the Hammers, can you name the opposition?

969. How many full England caps did Tony win: seven, eight or nine?

970. At which club did Tony venture into management in 2000/01?

971. On how many occasions have the Hammers been involved in the end-of-season play-offs?

972. Who did the Hammers face in their first-ever play-off fixture?

973. Can you name the side that West Ham faced in their first play-off final?

974. What was the venue for the Hammers' first play-off final appearance in 2004?

975. In which season did the Hammers first win promotion via the play-offs?

976. Who was the West Ham manager that led the club to their play-off final victory over Preston North End?

977. Can you name the Hammers' goalscorer from that game?

978. Each time the Hammers have qualified for the play-offs they have always reached the final, true or false?

979. En route to play-off glory in 2011/12, who did the Hammers defeat in the semi-final?

980. Who scored the Hammers' late winner in the 2011/12 Play-Off final victory over Blackpool?

QUIZ 99
BILLY BONDS

981. From which club did West Ham sign Billy?

982. Can you recall the transfer fee the Hammers paid for him?

983. Who was the first West Ham manager that Billy played under?

984. In which position did Billy play during his first three seasons at the club?

985. In what season did Billy top the Hammers' league scoring charts with 13 goals?

986. Against which club did Billy net the only hat-trick of his career: Coventry City, Charlton Athletic or Chelsea?

987. In what year did Billy become West Ham captain?

988. Billy captained the club in all three of their FA Cup final triumphs, true or false?

989. Billy holds the record for the most league appearances for the Hammers. How many league games did he play: 643, 653 or 663?

990. During which season did Billy become West Ham manager?

PAOLO DI CANIO

991. In which season did Di Canio join the Hammers?

992. From which club did the Hammers sign Paolo?

993. Before joining West Ham can you name the referee that Paolo pushed to the ground that resulted in him serving a lengthy ban?

994. Can you recall the transfer fee that West Ham paid to sign Paolo?

995. Who was the Hammers' boss when Paolo arrived at Upton Park?

996. Against which club did he score his first goal for West Ham?

997. In 1999/2000 Paolo scored a flying volley against Wimbledon, what award did that goal win?

998. How many goals did Paolo score in total during his West Ham career: 50, 51 or 52?

999. Which London club did he join after leaving West Ham in 2003?

1000. At which club did he begin his managerial career?

ANSWERS

QUIZ 1 · MARKO ARNAUTOVIC

1. Stoke City
2. Austria
3. Inter Milan
4. Werder Bremen
5. Manchester United
6. Chelsea
7. Bobby Zamora in 2006/07
8. Wales
9. He scored
10. He was Hammer of the Year

QUIZ 2 · SIR TREVOR BROOKING

11. Five times
12. Glenn Roeder
13. Right wing
14. They are the only players to have made more appearances for the club
15. Over (102)
16. 1972/73
17. 1980
18. Under (47)
19. 1984
20. Brooks

QUIZ 3 · FRANK LAMPARD SENIOR

21. Left-back
22. Twice
23. Southend United
24. Bobby Moore
25. Harry Redknapp
26. Brendan Rodgers
27. Jamie Redknapp
28. Twice
29. Ron Greenwood
30. Frank Junior played 647 times, Frank Senior played 584

QUIZ 4 · FRANK LAMPARD JUNIOR

31. Swansea City
32. Coventry City
33. The League Cup
34. 1998/99
35. Metz
36. Bradford City
37. Harry Redknapp
38. Over (106)
39. New York City
40. Derby County

QUIZ 5 · ANDRIY YARMOLENKO

41. Borussia Dortmund
42. Dynamo Kiev
43. Ukraine
44. England
45. True, V Luxembourg in 2014
46. Liverpool
47. Four times
48. Wales
49. Spurs
50. Bayern Munich

QUIZ 6 · BOBBY MOORE

51. Chelsea
52. OBE
53. 108
54. Malcolm Allison
55. 22
56. Footballer of the Year
57. The League Cup
58. He scored his two international goals against them
59. Billy Wright
60. Fulham

QUIZ 7 · ISSA DIOP

61. Toulouse
62. £20m
63. Arsenal
64. AFC Wimbledon

65. The Carabao Cup
66. France
67. Senegal
68. Bordeaux
69. Taller. Diop is 1.94, Carroll 1.93 & Reid 1.91
70. Wolves

QUIZ 8 · RON GREENWOOD

71. 1961
72. Chelsea
73. Doncaster
74. Arsenal
75. Three
76. Don Revie
77. John Lyall
78. Burnley
79. Wembley
80. B international

QUIZ 9 · LUKASZ FABIANSKI

81. Arsenal
82. Legia Warsaw
83. Poland
84. Arsene Wenger
85. 2014, for Arsenal
86. 1985
87. Artur Boruc
88. One
89. Swansea City
90. Liverpool

QUIZ 10 · GEOFF HURST

91. West Germany
92. Sunderland
93. Republic of Ireland, with Cork Celtic
94. South Africa, with Cape Town (On loan)
95. Seattle Sounders
96. 49
97. Essex
98. Kuwait
99. Chelsea
100. Stoke City

QUIZ 11 · JOHN SISSONS

101. 1963/64
102. The UEFA European U18 Championship in a 4-0 win for England against Spain
103. 53
104. Sheffield Wednesday
105. Chelsea
106. Norwich City
107. Tampa Bay Rowdies
108. South Africa, with Cape Town City
109. The League Cup
110. Geoff Hurst

QUIZ 12 · SUBSTITUTES

111. Peter Bennett, at Leeds, in August 1965
112. Bobby Gould, v Fulham in 1975
113. Bobby Zamora in the 71st minute of the 2006 final against Liverpool
114. Alan Taylor
115. Paul Brush
116. David Moyes, in January 2018
117. True
118. Bobby Gould
119. Ten
120. All of them

QUIZ 13 · FORMER GROUNDS

121. The Boleyn Ground
122. Hermit Road
123. Arsenal
124. The Cinder Heap
125. Browning Road
126. The Memorial Grounds
127. Brentford
128. Swindon Town
129. 1904
130. 2016

QUIZ 14 · 1963/64

131. The FA Cup
132. Preston North End
133. The League Cup
134. Leyton Orient
135. Johnny Byrne
136. Blackburn Rovers

137. Ron Greenwood
138. Leyton Orient
139. The League Cup,
by 20 to 19
140. Manchester United

QUIZ 15 · JOHN LYALL

141. 1974
142. England Youths,
against Luxembourg
143. The FA Youth Cup final,
against Manchester Utd
144. 1960
145. Third
146. The FA Cup
147. Lou Macari
148. Ipswich Town
149. Alan Devonshire
150. False, he managed
in 770 games, 29 fewer
than Bonds played

QUIZ 16 · FELIPE ANDERSON

151. Brazilian
152. Santos
153. Lazio
154. £36m
155. The Olympics
156. Liverpool
157. Carlos Tevez
158. One
159. The Europa League
160. 25

QUIZ 17 · MANUEL PELLEGRINI

161. Ripamonti
162. China
163. Manchester City
164. 2013/14
165. The League Cup
166. The League Cup
167. Chile
168. Italy
169. Real Madrid
170. Four

QUIZ 18 · 2017/18

171. Slaven Bilic
172. David Moyes
173. November
174. 13th
175. Werder Bremen
176. Huddersfield Town
177. Tottenham
in the League Cup
178. Shrewsbury Town
179. Enner Valencia
180. Joe Hart

QUIZ 19 · 2018/19

181. Manuel Pellegrini
182. Mainz 05
183. Marko Arnautovic
184. AFC Wimbledon
185. Issa Diop
186. Lukasz Fabianski

187. Jack Wilshere
188. Cheikhou Kouyate
189. Jordan Hugill
190. Winston Reid

QUIZ 20 · THE TWENTIES

191. 1923
192. Bolton Wanderers, who won 2-0
193. Promotion
194. Syd King
195. Vic Watson
196. Arsenal
197. Twice
198. Chelsea's Stamford Bridge
199. More: 65
200. Ten

QUIZ 21 · MARTIN PETERS

201. Second
202. Right foot
203. 33
204. Sir Alf Ramsey
205. 22
206. 1966
207. 20
208. West Germany
209. Tottenham Hotspur
210. Jimmy Greaves

QUIZ 22 · JOE COLE

211. The FA Cup
212. 1999

213. Bradford City
214. 2003
215. Chelsea
216. 2008
217. Liverpool
218. Lille
219. 2013
220. Over, he won 56

QUIZ 23 · THE WHITE HORSE FINAL

221. 1923
222. The FA Cup
223. Wembley (Empire Stadium also acceptable)
224. None
225. Bolton Wanderers
226. Bolton 2-0 West Ham
227. David Jack
228. Syd King
229. Billie (Billy acceptable)
230. George Scorey

QUIZ 24 · ATTENDANCES

231. Tottenham Hotspur
232. 1970
233. 42,322
234. Doncaster Rovers
235. Manchester United
236. Bolton Wanderers
237. The first ever Wembley FA Cup final in 1923
238. 100,000

239. 1975 against Ipswich recorded more than 1980 against Everton, 103,344 to 88,405
240. 1965, 100,000 compared to 58,000 in 1976

QUIZ 25 · LOU MACARI

241. 1989
242. Paul Ince
243. Mark Ward
244. Edinburgh
245. Celtic
246. Manchester United
247. Manchester United
248. Swindon Town
249. Ludek Miklosko
250. Stoke City

QUIZ 26 · DAVID MOYES

251. 2017/18
252. Preston North End
253. Division Two with Preston in 1999/2000
254. Under 18
255. Slaven Bilic
256. Real Sociedad
257. Cambridge United
258. No, he won nine and lost twelve of his 31 games
259. None, he was dismissed after eleven months
260. It was his 200th Premier League win

QUIZ 27 · FRANK McAVENNIE

261. Glasgow
262. St Mirren
263. Celtic
264. St Mirren & Celtic
265. Swindon Town
266. Cliftonville
267. South China of Hong Kong
268. Falkirk
269. Aston Villa
270. 1990/91

QUIZ 28 · BRYAN 'POP' ROBSON

271. 1972/73
272. 28
273. Two
274. Newcastle United
275. Sunderland
276. Nottingham Forest
277. Chelsea
278. Carlisle United
279. Under 23
280. He played most in his first section, 120 league games to 107

QUIZ 29 · VIC KEEBLE

281. The 1950s
282. Newcastle United
283. John Dick

284. Colchester United
285. Ted Fenton
286. 49
287. Blackpool
288. Blackburn Rovers
289. Arsenal
290. 29

QUIZ 30 · THE THIRTIES

291. Charlie Paynter
292. Syd King
293. The semi-final in 1933
294. Everton
295. Liverpool
296. First
297. Second
298. Vic Watson
299. Tottenham Hotspur
300. He was a qualified doctor

QUIZ 31 · ROBERT GREEN

301. Norwich City
302. Fewer, 219
303. QPR
304. Leeds United
305. Huddersfield Town
306. Chelsea
307. 2007/08
308. 2007/08
309. Twelve
310. Eleven

QUIZ 32 · LUDEK MIKLOSKO

311. Lou Macari
312. Oldham Athletic
313. Ian Bishop
314. Two: Steve Potts and Kevin Keen
315. Derby County
316. QPR
317. Banik Ostrava
318. Czechoslovakia
319. Goalkeeping coach
320. 1991

QUIZ 33 · ERNIE GREGORY

321. Goalkeeper
322. Two
323. 1946/47
324. 1959/60
325. 'B' international
326. The Isthmian League
327. They were the opponents for his testimonial
328. Five
329. 1957/58
330. The English Schools Trophy

QUIZ 34 · JOHNNY BYRNE

331. Budgie
332. Crystal Palace
333. Ron Brett
334. Crystal Palace

335. Crystal Palace
336. Fulham
337. South Africa
338. Eight
339. Portugal
340. 1963/64

QUIZ 35 · MATTHEW UPSON

341. Six
342. Four
343. None
344. Luton Town
345. MK Dons
346. Birmingham City
347. 15
348. Stoke City
349. 21
350. Over, he won 14 of his 21 caps while with West Ham

QUIZ 36 · VALON BEHRAMI

351. Switzerland
352. Lazio
353. Fiorentina
354. 2008
355. Watford
356. Hamburger SV
357. Napoli - the 2013/14 Coppa Italia
358. Manchester City

359. Wigan Athletic
360. Four

QUIZ 37 · SCOTT PARKER

361. 2007
362. Julian Dicks
363. Three
364. 2010/11
365. Charlton Athletic
366. 18
367. Three
368. Norwich City
369. Newcastle United
370. Five

QUIZ 38 · DYLAN TOMBIDES

371. 38
372. Australia
373. 20
374. Under 23
375. The Premier League
376. Wigan Athletic
377. Testicular cancer
378. Mark Noble
379. Taylor Tombides
380. Bobby Moore

QUIZ 39 · TONY GALE

381. Fulham
382. More: 300
383. 1984
384. Gary Crosby of Nottingham Forest

385. Paul Ince, then of Manchester United
386. Reggie - because his teammates said he reminded them of Reggie Kray
387. Under 21
388. Crystal Palace
389. Maidenhead United
390. Walton Casuals

QUIZ 40 · THE FORTIES

391. Charlie Paynter
392. Fulham
393. Wembley
394. Blackburn Rovers
395. Zero
396. Five
397. Peter Doherty
398. True
399. Division Two
400. Four

QUIZ 41 · ANDY MALCOLM

401. 1957/58
402. 1953/54
403. 1961/62
404. Twice: 1957/58 & 1958/59
405. Chelsea
406. Ron Tindall
407. QPR
408. Smiler

409. South Africa
410. Maldon

QUIZ 42 · HERITA ILUNGA

411. 2008
412. Toulouse
413. George McCartney, who returned to Sunderland
414. The FA Cup
415. Doncaster Rovers
416. Sam Allardyce
417. Nantes
418. Espanyol B
419. Saint-Etienne
420. DR Congo

QUIZ 43 · RONNIE BOYCE

421. Ticker
422. 17
423. He scored the winning goal
424. He scored twice
425. Under: 29 goals in 339 games in all competitions
426. Twice: 1963/64 & 1964/65
427. 1960/61
428. 1972/73
429. Youth and schoolboy level
430. La Gantoise

QUIZ 44 · YOSSI BENAYOUN

431. 1980

432. Israel
433. Ajax
434. Racing Santander
435. 2005
436. Alan Pardew
437. 2006
438. Liverpool
439. Chelsea
440. Over: 102

QUIZ 45 · AARON CRESSWELL

441. Ipswich Town
442. 2014/15
443. Tranmere Rovers
444. Spain
445. Manchester City
446. Leicester City
447. Newcastle United
448. 2008
449. Ipswich Town
450. Liverpool

QUIZ 46 · JAVIER HERNANDEZ

451. Geoff Hurst
452. South Korea
453. 2017
454. Manchester United
455. Real Madrid
456. David Moyes
457. Bayer Leverkusen
458. Chicharito

459. Little pea
460. Southampton

QUIZ 47 · EYAL BERKOVIC

461. Southampton
462. Israel
463. Harry Redknapp
464. Tottenham Hotspur
465. Celtic
466. Manchester City
467. Portsmouth
468. Three
469. Derby County
470. Under, he netted a dozen times

QUIZ 48 · MICHAEL CARRICK

471. Wallsend Boys Club
472. The FA Youth Cup
473. The Intertoto Cup
474. Swindon Town
475. Birmingham City
476. Tottenham Hotspur
477. Manchester United
478. 34
479. Sven-Goran Eriksson
480. Crystal Palace

QUIZ 49 · MANUEL LANZINI

481. Argentina
482. River Plate
483. Everton

484. Huddersfield Town
485. Europa League
486. Liverpool
487. Michail Antonio
488. Brazil
489. Italy
490. Al Jazira

QUIZ 50 · THE FIFTIES

491. Ted Fenton
492. 1957/58
493. Four
494. Aston Villa
495. Don Revie
496. Malcolm Allison
497. Fulham
498. John Dick
499. Frank O'Farrell
500. Over - 101

QUIZ 51 · PHIL PARKES

501. Walsall
502. Queens Park Rangers
503. John Lyall
504. True
505. Oldham Athletic
506. Three
507. Phil (he played 440 games to Robert Green's 241)
508. Portugal
509. One
510. Ipswich Town

QUIZ 52 · JOHN BOND

511. 1952
512. Right-back
513. Eight
514. One
515. 381
516. Torquay United
517. Bournemouth
518. Ken Brown
519. 1980/81
520. He ran a sweet shop

QUIZ 53 · CRAIG BELLAMY

521. Cardiff
522. Norwich City
523. Liverpool
524. £7.5M
525. Manchester City
526. Bristol Rovers
527. Chelsea
528. 26
529. Manchester City
530. Craig (he won 78 Welsh caps to James Collins' 51)

QUIZ 54 · JOHN McDOWELL

531. Ron Greenwood
532. Blackpool
533. 1971/72
534. Newcastle United
535. Nine
536. Newport County
537. Over 300 (303)

538. John Bond
539. £20,000
540. Bristol Rovers

QUIZ 55 · TED FENTON

541. 1932
542. Carrow Road (Norwich City)
543. 170
544. Colchester United
545. Charlie Paynter
546. 1950
547. Blackburn Rovers
548. True
549. Ron Greenwood
550. Southend United

QUIZ 56 · ALAN DEVONSHIRE

551. 1956
552. Crystal Palace
553. Southall
554. £5,000
555. Queens Park Rangers
556. 1980/81
557. Six
558. Elland Road
559. He wore the number six shirt
560. Watford

QUIZ 57 · KEITH ROBSON

561. Newcastle United
562. 1974

563. John Lyall
564. £60,000
565. Tranmere Rovers
566. Leicester City
567. 2-2
568. Keith (he made 89 appearances to Stewart Robson's 84)
569. True
570. Cardiff City

QUIZ 58 · HAMMER OF THE YEAR

571. 1957/58
572. The fans
573. Andy Malcolm
574. 1961/62
575. Lawrie Leslie
576. 1960/61
577. Alvin Martin
578. 2002/03
579. Twice
580. Michail Antonio

QUIZ 59 · LIAM BRADY

581. Arsenal
582. Republic of Ireland
583. Italy
584. 1986/87
585. Norwich City
586. Ten exactly
587. Wolverhampton Wanderers

588. Three (John Lyall, Lou Macari and Billy Bonds)
589. Celtic
590. Brighton & Hove Albion

QUIZ 60 · THE 1960s

591. Ron Greenwood
592. Quarter-final (knocked out by Liverpool)
593. Johnny Byrne (33 goals in all competitions)
594. 1961/62 & 1968/69
595. Ken Brown
596. Three times
597. Trevor Brooking
598. West Bromwich Albion
599. Frank McAvennie
600. Nottingham Forest

QUIZ 61 · TREVOR MORLEY

601. Northampton Town
602. True
603. Howard Kendall
604. Leicester City
605. Hull City
606. 17
607. 15
608. Anglo-Italian Cup (v Reggiana)
609. Above (Sissons scored 53 goals for the Hammers)
610. 1993/94

QUIZ 62 · JUST THE ONCE

611. Dale Gordon
612. Mick Beesley
613. True
614. Sebastien Carole
615. Danny Collins
616. Macclesfield Town
617. Keith Rowland
618. Pelly Ruddock
619. Hull City
620. Aston Villa

QUIZ 63 · BOXING DAY FIXTURES

621. AFC Bournemouth
622. Swansea City
623. Tottenham Hotspur
624. Wimbledon
625. Ipswich Town
626. West Ham United 2 Oldham Athletic 0
627. Ipswich Town
628. Paul Kitson
629. Keith Robson
630. True

QUIZ 64 · FA CUP WINNERS 1964

631. True
632. Charlton Athletic
633. Geoff Hurst
634. Johnny Byrne
635. Burnley

636. True
637. West Ham United 0
Manchester United 2
638. Hillsborough
639. Howard Kendall
(a record he held until
it was superseded by
Paul Allen in 1980)
640. 90th minute

QUIZ 65 · 1965 EUROPEAN CUP WINNERS' CUP

641. The FA Cup
642. Ronnie Boyce
643. Away to Gent
(first round, first leg)
644. West Ham United 3
Sparta Prague 2
645. Lausanne
646. Brian Dear
647. Under 35,000 (34,864)
648. 1860 Munich
649. Wembley
650. Alan Sealey

QUIZ 66 · HAMMERS AT THE WORLD CUP

651. Liverpool &
Manchester United
652. Bobby Moore
653. False (only Bobby Moore
started the first game)
654. Four
655. 78th minute

656. True
657. Two (Bobby Moore
& Geoff Hurst, Martin
Peters had since joined
Tottenham Hotspur)
658. Trevor Brooking
659. Paraguay
660. False (Michael Owen
was the youngest
member of the squad)

QUIZ 67 · INTERNATIONALS

661. John Harkes
662. Five
663. True
664. Davor Suker
665. Peru
666. Danny Gabbidon
667. Angelo Ogbonna
668. Senegal
669. Lionel Messi
670. Carlos Tevez

QUIZ 68 · OPENING DAY FIXTURES

671. Manuel Pellegrini
672. 2015/16
(away to Arsenal)
673. Teddy Sheringham
674. Wrexham
675. James Collins
676. Victoria Ground
(Stoke City)
677. Dean Ashton

678. David Connolly
679. Manchester United
680. Notts County

QUIZ 69 · REPRESENTATIVE GAMES AT THE BOLEYN

681. 2014
682. Croatia
683. Yes, the winner from a penalty in a 2-1 win
684. Javier Mascherano
685. Stan Lazaridis of Australia
686. Paul Konchesky
687. Dereck Chisora
688. Dulwich Hamlet
689. Frank Lampard junior
690. Luxembourg

QUIZ 70 · THE 1970s

691. Alan Stephenson
692. Burnley & Blackpool
693. Sixth
694. Norwich City
695. Three
696. Malky Mackay
697. Martin Peters
698. Stoke City
699. Old Trafford
700. Glenn Roeder

QUIZ 71 · JOHN HARTSON

701. Swansea

702. Luton Town
703. The £2.5M fee set a new record for a British teenager
704. George Graham
705. Derby County
706. 14th
707. Five goals
708. Huddersfield Town (League Cup)
709. 14
710. Five (Wimbledon, Coventry City, Celtic, West Bromwich Albion & Norwich City)

QUIZ 72 · LEAGUE CUP CAMPAIGNS

711. 1965/66
712. West Bromwich Albion
713. Two (Charlton Athletic & Tottenham Hotspur)
714. Paul Goddard & Jimmy Neighbour
715. Les Sealy
716. Clive Thomas
717. Ray Stewart
718. Villa Park
719. Paul Goddard
720. 1989/90

QUIZ 73 · MARK WARD

721. Liverpool

722. Everton
723. Baker
724. FA Trophy Final
725. Oldham Athletic
726. Paul Allen
727. £250,000
728. True
729. Ian Bishop
& Trevor Morley
730. Howard Kendall

QUIZ 74 · ALVIN MARTIN

731. Ipswich Town
732. Aston Villa
733. Shirt number five
734. Leeds United
735. 17
736. Mexico 1986
737. Martin Thomas (who was then injured), Chris Hedworth (who replaced Thomas before suffering injury himself) & Peter Beardsley (who replaced Hedworth)
738. In fifth place. Only Billy Bonds, Frank Lampard (Snr), Bobby Moore and Trevor Brooking sit above him
739. Sheffield Wednesday
740. Southend United

QUIZ 75 · FA CUP WINNERS

741. Southampton
742. Trevor Brooking & Pat Holland
743. Queens Park Rangers
744. Alan Taylor
745. Villa Park
746. 0-0
747. Stamford Bridge
748. True
749. Fulham
750. Six

QUIZ 76 · 1975/79 EUROPEAN CUP WINNERS' CUP

751. Finland
752. 5-2
753. Armenia
754. Ron Greenwood
755. Aad Mansveld
756. Billy Jennings
757. Alan Taylor
758. Eintracht Frankfurt
759. Heysel Stadium
760. West Ham United 2 Anderlecht 4

QUIZ 77 · JULIAN DICKS

761. £300,000
762. Left-back
763. Five
764. Arsenal

765. Two
766. True
767. 326
768. True
769. Mike Marsh
   & David Burrows
770. Four times (1990,
   1992, 1996 & 1997)

QUIZ 78 · DIMITRI PAYET

771. French
772. Marseille
773. Slaven Bilic
774. Arsenal
775. Leicester City
776. Newcastle United
777. AFC Bournemouth
778. Two
779. Michail Antonio
780. £25M

QUIZ 79 · DEAN ASHTON

781. Crewe Alexandra
782. Norwich City
783. Alan Pardew
784. Three
785. Arsenal
786. Sunderland
787. Trinidad & Tobago
788. Pepe Reina
789. 19
790. He scored with a
   spectacular overhead kick

QUIZ 80 · FA CUP WINNERS 1980

791. True
792. Second Division
793. West Bromwich Albion
794. Orient 2
   West Ham United 3
795. Swansea City
796. Ray Stewart
797. Villa Park
798. Frank Lampard
799. 13th minute
800. George Courtney

QUIZ 81 · THE EIGHTIES

801. Notts County
   & Swansea City
802. 58
803. Stoke City
804. Alvin Martin
805. Frank Lampard
806. Tony Cottee
807. Birmingham City
808. Steve Walford
809. Newcastle United
   & Middlesbrough
810. Luton Town

QUIZ 82 · DAVID CROSS

811. Rochdale
812. Norwich City
813. West Bromwich Albion
814. £180,000

815. True
816. 22
817. He became the first, and only player to-date, to score a hat-trick for West Ham in European competition
818. David (he scored 97 to Paul Goddard's 71)
819. Tottenham Hotspur
820. Manchester City

QUIZ 83 · SAM ALLARDYCE

821. Bolton Wanderers
822. Blackburn Rovers
823. Get the club back into the Premier League ASAP!
824. George McCartney
825. Malky Mackay
826. Kevin Nolan
827. Reading & Southampton
828. Tenth place
829. False (Sam was Manager of the Month but with four wins and one draw)
830. 13th place

QUIZ 84 · JERMAIN DEFOE

831. Charlton Athletic
832. Walsall
833. True
834. AFC Bournemouth
835. Ipswich Town
836. He submitted a written transfer request within 24 hours of relegation
837. 41
838. Portsmouth
839. Sweden
840. Toronto FC

QUIZ 85 · KEN BROWN

841. Centre-half
842. Neville United
843. 474
844. True
845. England
846. Billy Bonds
847. John Bond
848. Kenny
849. League (Milk) Cup
850. Lifetime Achievement Award

QUIZ 86 · THE 1985/86 SEASON

851. Third in the First Division
852. Four points
853. Frank McAvennie (28 goals in all competitions)
854. 46 goals
855. St Andrew's (Birmingham City)
856. Ray Stewart & Geoff Pike
857. Sheffield Wednesday

858. Newcastle United
859. 84 points
860. Tony Cottee

QUIZ 87 · MARK NOBLE

861. Arsenal
862. 15 years old
863. Southend United
864. League Cup
865. Molineux (Wolverhampton Wanderers)
866. Ipswich Town
867. Brighton & Hove Albion
868. Birmingham City
869. Watford
870. True

QUIZ 88 · RIO FERDINAND

871. 1978
872. Gavin
873. Tony Cottee
874. Sheffield Wednesday
875. Blackburn Rovers
876. Frank Lampard (Jnr)
877. 1997/98
878. Leeds United
879. Six
880. Anton (he made 163 appearances to Rio's 158)

QUIZ 89 · ANDY CARROLL

881. Gateshead
882. Preston North End

883. Liverpool
884. Seven goals
885. Swansea City
886. £15M
887. 2015/16 (nine goals)
888. Four
889. True
890. France

QUIZ 90 · THE 1990s

891. Tony Gale
892. Villa Park
893. Ronnie Boyce
894. Ian Wright
895. Torquay United
896. Tottenham Hotspur
897. True
898. Fifth
899. John Hartson
900. Derby County

QUIZ 91 · THE 1990/91 SEASON

901. Billy Bonds
902. Midlesbrough
903. Barnsley
904. Ludek Miklosko
905. Trevor Morley
906. Twelve goals
907. Swindon Town
908. Five
909. Oldham Athletic
910. Ludek Miklosko

QUIZ 92 · PAUL INCE

911. False (he supported West Ham)
912. Full Members Cup (v Chelsea)
913. Newcastle United
914. Under 100 (95)
915. 1988/89
916. Liverpool
917. Manchester United
918. Spain
919. Inter Milan
920. Milton Keynes Dons

QUIZ 93 · THE 1992/93 SEASON

921. Harry Redknapp
922. Clive Allen
923. Kevin Keen and Steve Potts
924. Ludek Miklosko
925. False (Trevor Morley was top scorer)
926. David Speedie
927. Crewe Alexandra
928. Cambridge United
929. Newcastle United
930. Portsmouth

QUIZ 94 · THE 1993/94 SEASON

931. True
932. Joey Beauchamp
933. Sheffield Wednesday
934. Lee Chapman
935. Liverpool
936. Norwich City
937. One point
938. 13th place
939. 16 goals
940. Ipswich Town

QUIZ 95 · RAY STEWART

941. Dundee United
942. Kenny Dalglish
943. He was voted the Scottish Professional Football Association Young Player of the Year
944. £430,000
945. True
946. John Lyall
947. 76
948. He was the only non-English player in the Hammers' team
949. He was nicknamed 'Tonka' after Tonka Toys which were described as 'indestructible'
950. St Johnstone

QUIZ 96 · EUROPA LEAGUE

951. Slaven Bilic
952. Reece Oxford
953. Andora

954. Diafra Sakho
955. True
956. Astra Giurgiu
957. He scored the Hammers' final European goal at Upton Park
958. It was the club's first game at the London Stadium
959. Cheikhou Kouyate
960. Domzale 2 West Ham United 1 (the Hammers won 4-2 on aggregate)

QUIZ 97 · TONY COTTEE

961. Forest Gate
962. 17 years old
963. Tottenham Hotspur
964. Frank McAvennie
965. Everton
966. £2.2M
967. 1985/86
968. Queens Park Rangers
969. Seven
970. Barnet

QUIZ 98 · PLAY-OFFS

971. Three times
972. Ipswich Town
973. Crystal Palace
974. Millennium Stadium (Cardiff)

975. 2004/05
976. Alan Pardew
977. Bobby Zamora
978. True
979. Cardiff City
980. Ricardo Vaz Te

QUIZ 99 · BILLY BONDS

981. Charlton Athletic
982. £50,000
983. Ron Greenwood
984. Right-back
985. 1973/74
986. Chelsea
987. 1974
988. False (he was captain in two of the three FA Cup Final victories)
989. 663
990. 1989/90

QUIZ 100 · PAOLO DI CANIO

991. 1999
992. Sheffield Wednesday
993. Paul Alcock
994. £1.7M
995. Harry Redknapp
996. Blackburn Rovers
997. It was voted the BBC's Goal of the Season
998. 51
999. Charlton Athletic
1000. Swindon Town